HOW TO WORK SHEET METAL

HOW TO WORK
SHEET METAL

A practical man's description of metal working practice "straight from the bench"

HERBERT J. DYER

MODEL & ALLIED PUBLICATIONS
ARGUS BOOKS LIMITED
Argus House, St James Road, Watford,
Hertfordshire, England

Model and Allied Publications
Argus Books Ltd.
Argus House, 14 St James Road, Watford,
Hertfordshire, England

First Published 1948
Second Impression 1951
Third Impression 1955
Fourth Impression 1963
Fifth Impression 1968
Sixth Impression 1971
Seventh Impression 1972
Eighth Impression 1974
Ninth Impression 1979

ISBN 0 85344 121 9

Printed by A. Wheaton & Co. Ltd., Exeter

PREFACE

THE simple sheet metal working hints and instructions in the ensuing pages are intended primarily for the " small " general jobbing shop, where it is imperative that a modicum of such knowledge be possessed by the owner or operative.

The methods described have been used on and off by me for close on a quarter of a century—at any rate since I first began to serve my time in a shop where I was given insight into sheet metal-work besides the usual fitting and turning, because sheet metal working was as essential to the shop's products as the more mechanical operations.

The tools, or many of them, shown in further pages, have been evolved to suit my own needs in the absence of the tool or machine usually associated with a particular process or job. Maybe because they were cheaper ; possibly because the job was wanted " at once " and there was no time to purchase such a tool ; or perhaps there was not such a tool—or one in such a size—to be had for that job alone.

It is hoped, then, that by the time you, the reader, have read through the following pages you may have picked up more than one useful tip, or at the least that you may have been pleasurably entertained. With this object in mind, as well as instruction, all unnecessary technicalities have been avoided.

H. J. DYER.

CONTENTS

HOW TO WORK SHEET METAL

CHAPTER I

SIMPLE SHEET METAL-WORKING EQUIPMENT

BEFORE any work can be done at all there must be a bench on which to do it. Out of many benches—some good and others rotten in every sense of the word—the only one which has given me any satisfaction is one made by myself to suit myself.

The Bench

Along the side wall of the shop, 6 in. lower than the window ledge, is the bench top. It is 6 ft. long and is made of three thicknesses of 1 in. tongue and groove timber—as used for flooring. The top and bottom longitudinal boards are nailed to the shorter cross boards which are sandwiched between. Firstly, the long boards were fitted together on the floor, clamped together, and the short pieces nailed thereto with nails which just failed to come right through. If they do go through far, by the time three or four dozen are in, the maker will find it quite a job to raise the bench—he will have nailed it to the floor. Anyhow, having nailed the cross-members to the long ones, the next layer of long ones is again laid on to the " shorts " and again nailed. Next, raise and turn over and nail back through the first longs into the cross middle ones, so that there are heads on both sides of the bench.

People of a meticulous turn of mind may decry the nailing act as being slipshod. There is nothing against the job being screwed all over. A couple or so gross of $1\frac{3}{4}$ in. and $2\frac{1}{2}$ in. screws are cheap enough—relatively. Personally, I would rather drive that number of nails than screw-drive a like quantity of screws. The bench top, when completed, is fixed, one end against the end wall of the shop and screwed to angle iron at that end as well as at the back, the angle iron being screwed through the wall at, say, 18 in. intervals.

The legs of the bench are made up of steel 2 in. channel screwed to 2 in. angle at top and bottom, braced diagonally with $1\frac{1}{4}$ in. × $\frac{1}{4}$ in. flat bar. (See Fig. 1.) At points 12 in. and 24 in. from the bottom, angle irons are screwed to the legs back and front, which act as further braces and as bearers for the shelves under the bench. These shelves carry most of the impedimenta peculiar to sheet metal working, *i.e.*, an edging machine or jenny, swaging and wiring machines, tinners bars, stakes, and so on.

Along the front edge of the bench is a length of $2\frac{1}{2}$ in. equal angle iron, countersunk screwed to the top and front edge by $2\frac{1}{2}$ in. wood screws of some $\frac{1}{4}$ in. diameter—screws every 6 in. top and front alternately.

Drilled and tapped into this front angle are holes which are so spaced as to agree with others in a flat bar $\frac{1}{2}$ in. × $2\frac{1}{2}$ in., the same length as the bench front. The holes may be spaced say 6 in. apart, and be for $\frac{1}{2}$ in. Whit. bolts which pass through clearing holes in the bar into tapped ones in the angle face. This appliance is actually a very wide vice which will enable the operator to bend over a sheet of metal at right angles. There is the entire bench length, less 12 in., to work with as regards gripping capacity, and from the bench to floor or ceiling for space to handle a big sheet for bending. The *modus operandi* is shown in Fig. 2. At convenient points there may be socket holes for the reception of stakes and dollies and the tangs of various machines.

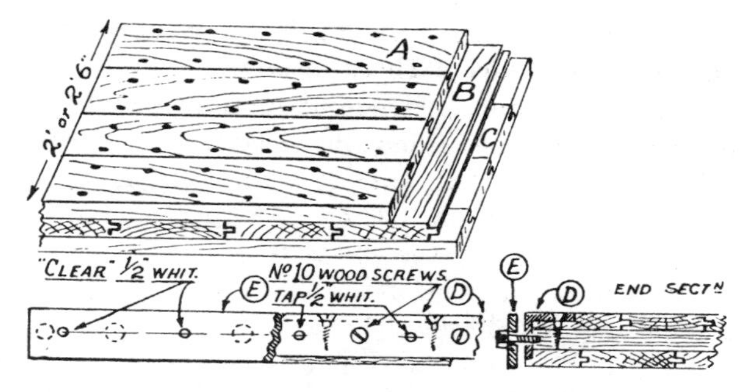

Nail or screw short battens B to longitudinals C, using cramp to secure meantime. Fix top longitudinals A thereto in like manner

Rabbet top and front edges and screw in place a length of angle iron D. Front face of this is also drilled and tapped at six-inch intervals for ½ in. whit. bolts which secure the "bending bar" E used for bending large sheets

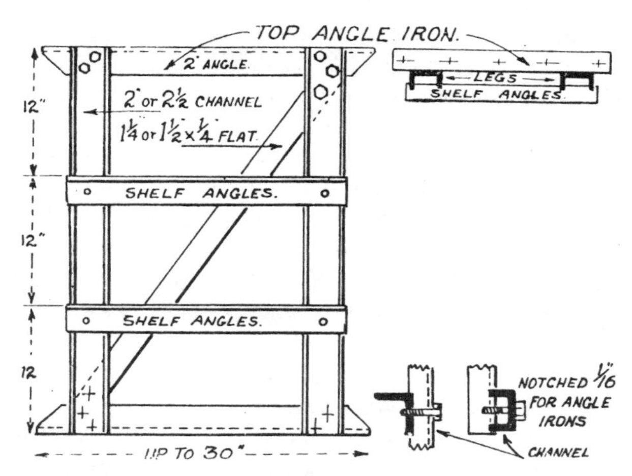

Top and bottom angles are screwed to channel iron legs "back to back." Shelf angles are then notched "back-on" into the edges of channels and the diagonal cross brace is fitted to contact tightly against the inner edges of the angle irons top and bottom, making a very rigid structure

Fig. 1.—Bench construction

It is wise to plate these socket holes, as otherwise they become badly worn from the continuous wobbling about of the tools in question. Where convenient, the tools may be held in a vice, thus avoiding their insertion in bench holes.

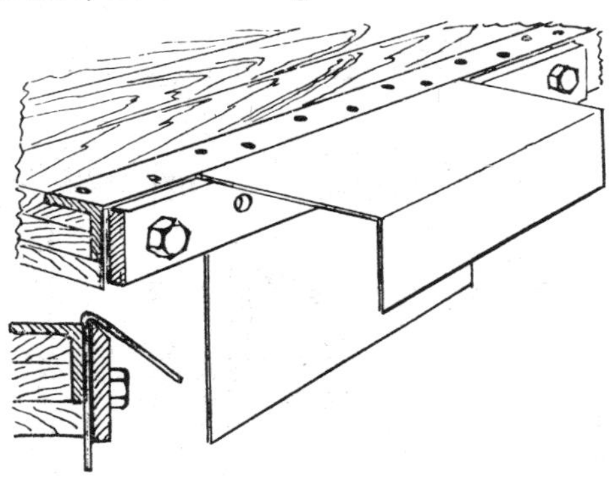

Preferably the same length as bench. That pair of bolts which comes close to the outer edges of the sheet metal should be used. A complete "box" may be formed thereon, or, by veeing the top edge of bar, angles of less than 90° may be folded over it

Fig. 2.—Clamp bar

A very convenient height for such a bench is about 3 ft., which is not too high for an operator of 5 ft. 7 in. Anything lower would be very low indeed, and a width of 2 ft. 6 in. gives plenty of room to work and easy access to the tool rack at the back. The bench as described may be altered in any way that may be desired as regards length or width or height, but be advised and keep it thick enough and retain the bread-and-butter construction and the iron legs if at all possible. It will not twist; it can be repaired—a couple of new front boards inserted—easily. Here is where the "screw-method" scores, though my own bench has seen ten years' work now and is not yet in need of re-boarding by a long way. A final point to recommend it is rigidity. It will neither bounce, spring, nor walk all over the shop—with the user pulling it back every now and then.

Tools

For the small user, many advise buying a meagre kit and waiting for the work to come in before getting the tools.

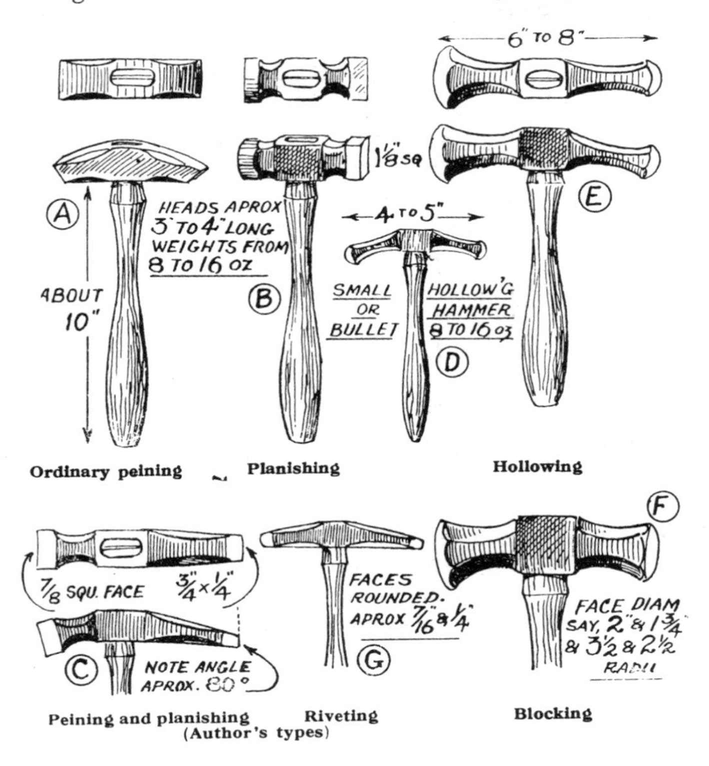

Fig. 3.—Types of hammers

This is sound, within limits. Suppose, however, you are asked to make a tank of such and such size, and you have to ask for time to look round and buy the kit necessary to swage the ends—or some such excuse ? By the time you have bought your kit, the client will have had his job done by someone else who already has his. It is better to have a tool than wish you had it. Solicitous and well-meaning but inquisitive folk have asked me: "Why don't you take on a helper instead of getting a machine?" They were blind to the fact that such a machine would enable one to do a type of work next to impossible by hand methods, and that to have it, even if rarely used, was an advantage in itself, especially as a *helper* could not do it anyway. So it may be seen that the possession of adequate tool equipment, either hand or machine, is advantageous.

Beginning with hand tools, a fair start may be made with a *Peining Hammer* of about 12 oz., shown in Fig. 3. Actually a square-faced hammer, one end is drawn out and ground off at an angle, which enables it to be used for knocking over the bottoms of containers and also for similar work on lids and the like; this connection will be enlarged upon later in "Seaming."

A *Planishing Hammer* may have a pair of square faces or one may be round; such a hammer, as its name implies, is for planishing or flattening sheet metals.

A *Hollowing Hammer* for the production of hollow or hemispherical forms is essential and varies from about 1½ lb. in a 1¼ in. diameter head to some 3 lb. in a 1¾ in. faced hammer. Weight, of course, varies with the lengths of heads and with the amount of metal actually in the head or eye portion. These tend to be deceiving. You need, perhaps, a type of head for a specific job, and find one sketched out and made by the people who cater for such tools. When it arrives, you may find that a hammer guessed at being 2 lb. or so is actually over three, and a "fair killer" to use for any length of time.

A *Blocking Hammer* is very similar to a hollowing type, but the degree of convexity of the faces is very much less, being required for smoothing out the uneven surface of a form left from a previous process.

For very small hollows, such as the little cup-like forms a milk-can stands on, and for similar work, a *Bullet* or

Studding Hammer is used. This varies from about 6 oz. to 1 lb. in weight, exclusive of the handle or shaft, or hilt, shank, helve or haft. I have heard all these terms used up and down the country. Then for riveting one needs a hammer or two. Some firms specify special *Tinman's Riveting* hammers, though why these people are supposed

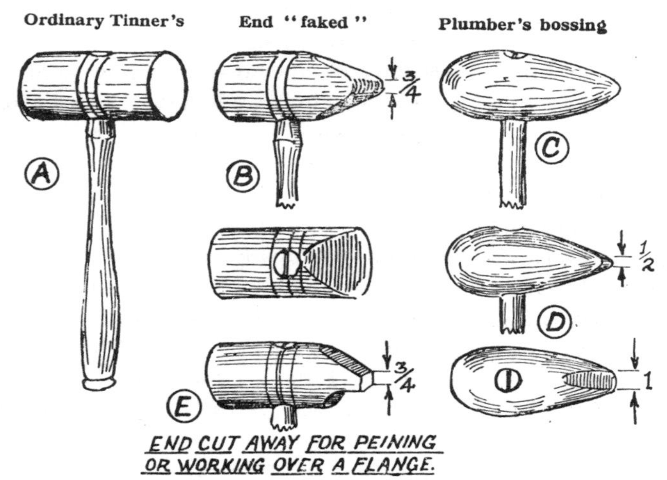

All usually from 2¼ to 3 in. dia., and made in "box" or lignum vitae. Bossing mallets usually have red cane handles

Fig. 4.—Mallets

to need a special type of hammer to hit their rivets with is hard to say.

I use the same hammers for sheet metal riveting as for any other riveting or light hammer work ; a pair of 4 oz. and 6 oz. ball-pein hammers of the slender-headed type, together with another 6 oz. cross-pein for working close in to a vertical surface, and a special double-ender, shown at the foot of Fig. 3.

Mallets

Two ordinary " Tinman's Boxwood " mallets (see Fig. 4) will be all that are needed in the flat-faced line. Their heads are like croquet mallets—the cylindrical one may be $2\frac{1}{4}$ in. or $2\frac{3}{4}$ in. diameter.

These are mainly used for flattening and generally working up jobs on the stakes or bar and for seaming or edging over on the " hatchet " stake or " half-moon " stake. Anyhow, a sheet metal worker cannot very well manage without them, so they are included in this list, also either one or a pair of *Plumbers' Bossing* mallets for hollow work. These have pear-shaped heads and are of lignum vitae or good boxwood, and often have cane handles; sizes vary from about $1\frac{3}{4}$ in. to $2\frac{1}{2}$ in. diameter at the large end.

Soft-faced Hammers

Many types of hammers fitted with soft faces are now available. The Thor Hammer Company manufacture copper-headed hammers from $\frac{3}{4}$ lb. to 15 lb., copper and rawhide hammers, rawhide hammers, light hammers with cellulose and nylon heads and rubber-faced hammers. These types of hammers are useful when dealing with very soft metals, where it is important that the material shall not be marked.

Snips

These (see Fig. 5) are so usual in almost any trade as to call for little comment. They may be had in various sizes from as small as 6 in. up to about 14 in. for the hand type, and still larger for the type which has a tang forged vertically on to the lower " handle." This tang may be set into a block, into a hole in the bench or in the " hardie " hole in an anvil, or may even be gripped in the vice. For general purposes, however, three pairs of ordinary pattern may be purchased. Sizes should be about 8 in. and 12 in. straight with a pair of 8 in. curved blades ; there are also made special patterns with peculiarly-shaped blades which will cut straight or intricately-curved paths through metal considerably thicker than is possible with the ordinary pattern. Holes may be cut in cylindrical bodies with equal facility, it being necessary to drill or chisel-cut just a single hole for starting from somewhere inside the part to be removed, preferably near the centre for a small aperture, but near the edge for a larger one, so that a certain amount of cut-away metal may be saved. In cutting a small hole it is more important to be able to operate the tool gradually and certainly towards the marked-out line than to save the metal that is cut out.

For small intricate work *Dental Snips* can be obtained

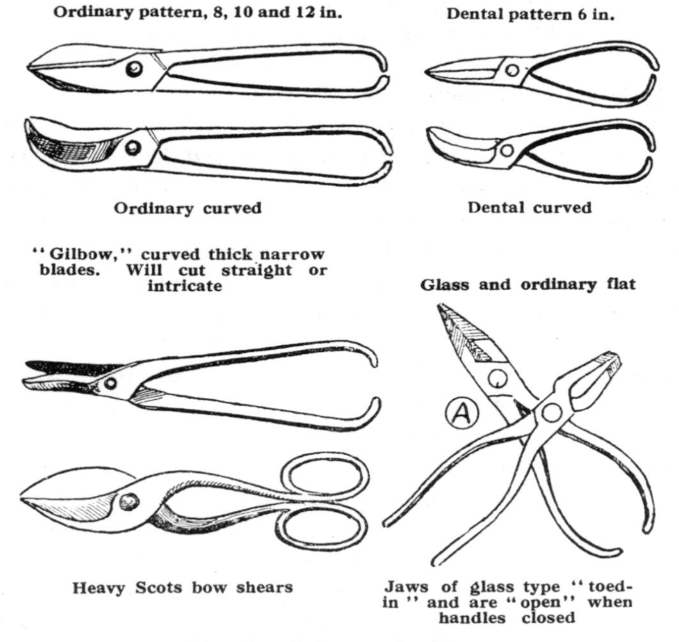

Fig. 5.—Snips and pliers

which have fairly long handles and short blades. The snips themselves are about 6 in. overall, both in curved and straight types. These are used a good deal in the art metal working trades.

Soldering Irons

In Fig. 6 may be seen a representative assortment of these tools. Why exactly they should be known as " irons " is not clear, as the bits themselves are of copper, the only iron parts being the rods securing them to the handles.

The sizes and weights given in the sketches may be varied to suit individual fancies or requirements.

For really serious repair work I rarely use less than a 3 lb. iron, though as time goes on this weight decreases owing to loss of metal through continued scaling due to the combined action of acid and heat. A pair of three-pounders, used alternately and heated over a Primus or other stove, will do all that may be required, keeping up enough heat to enable the user to solder all round a vessel—side and end seams—about 3 ft. long and 15 in. diameter, without having to wait for heat. The suitable weight of iron depends upon the mass of metal to be soldered. The quicker one wants the job, the smaller is the iron chosen, provided it is only a light job. There is no object in waiting for a two- or three-pounder to heat up if all one has to do is a split seam in, say, an oil can, after which there may be no further work immediately required. Having heated up a big iron for a heavy job, however, do not put it aside and heat up a small one just to do a wee job. Actually, a big iron is preferable, in as much as it seems easier to control, besides which it can be laid aside momentarily with but little loss of heat, while small adjustments of parts to be soldered are effected.

In Fig. 6D is a home-made iron for rivet-sweating. Easy to make, it may be of two styles, one as shown, and another bent at right angles, or with the rod set in the bit that way.

Simply heat up and tin ; apply flux to the rivet head and surrounding metal ; place a globule of solder (pea-size) close to the rivet, touch with the iron and transfer it and

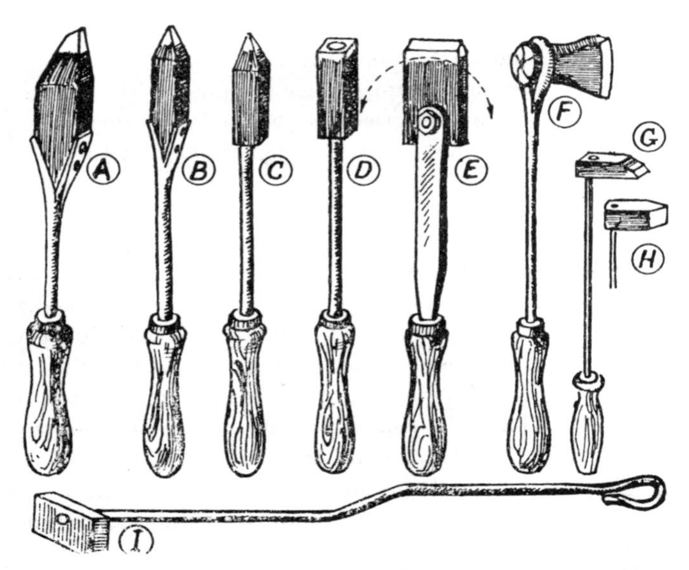

AB, ordinary type, heavy and medium, 3 lb. down to about 1 lb.; C, light "home-made," rod screwed into bit, 1 lb. down to 4 oz.; D, special "square" for sweating rivets, 1 lb. or 8 oz.; E, dual purpose "straight or hatchet" for seams, lids, etc.; F, regular type "hatchet," bit riveted into rod "eye," 1 to 2 lb.; GH, small irons for very light work, bits 1 to 2 oz.; I, special "long-reach" iron for inside work on tanks, etc. Handle rod may be bent to reach any desired location

Fig. 6.—Soldering irons

hold it over the rivet head, keeping it there a while—say fifteen seconds or so.

Fig. 6E is a hatchet bit, as also is that shown at F. The former is home-made, or rather, "shop"-made, and greatly facilitates running solder along a seam either inside or outside a job. One can turn it and lock it in any angular position. When one bit burns away it is easy to replace. At G and H are shown a couple of miniature ones for very small work, such as instrument or fancy-goods repairs. Being of small bulk they do not hold their heat at all well, whilst during the heating one must be very careful not to burn them and spoil their tinning—a mistake very easily made, should one's attention be drawn away.

The coal-rake or croupiers' money-pusher-like gadget, shown in Fig. 6I is very useful indeed. It has enabled its maker to solder defects that were voted impossible to repair.

Fluxes

Under this heading comes a whole host of proprietary brands, both pastes and liquids, each and all being very satisfactory in their spheres of application. "Baker's Soldering Fluid" is very good, and can be had in small tins or in half and whole gallon cans. Not so fiercely acid as the old spirits of salts, it can be safely carried round in the tool kit and a little poured out into a suitable receptacle whilst on the job. An egg-cup or a large dolls' tea-set cup is fine for the job—it holds just enough to preclude waste.

"Fluxite" is also very well known among the resinous paste fluxes, and is suitable for electrical repairs where no acid action is permissible afterwards.

Then there is "Tinol," which may be had in very convenient sizes, and will be found equally effective, directions on each container or carton giving the user every chance of successful work.

"Soldo" is yet another, besides which comes a number of resin or flux-filled hollow solder wires requiring no other flux. Very many makers state that no previous cleaning of the work is necessary to effect a satisfactory joint. Possibly this is correct in some cases, but it may be said that if an uncleaned joint will be effective, then one which has been thoroughly scraped up and cleaned *and* tinned is going to be a really good joint. As it is that sort we desire, the advice is herein given to clean thoroughly all surfaces to be joined and make success certain.

For galvanised iron, scrape the work clean and free from grease or soap, especially domestic ware. Use spirits of salts—hydrochloric acid in which scrap zinc has been dissolved until it will not take any more ; in very obstinate cases I use the neat acid. Mind the clothes and the skin and anything you value, because used thus it is very rapid in its action, and eats through anything.

Sal-ammoniac is also a flux which is useful for tinning copper and brass—many of the domestic pots and pans in large establishments and hotels were, and possibly still are, of copper, internally tinned, and the re-tinning of such was quite a nice source of revenue to the tinsmith of a few years ago—until aluminium became so popular for domestic cooking utensils.

Stakes

In Fig. 7 is shown a fairly representative assortment of these tools. It is quite safe to say that there are scores of others, but those shown will do all that the ordinary small user will ever be likely to need. The *Pepper Box* and *Dome Head* stakes A and B are for finishing to shape such forms as the names imply. The work is beaten over them with a mallet or hammer as will be shown later.

Sketches C, D, and E, are for flattening and truing up corners of " sided " articles. The *Canister Stake* is particularly useful for edging over small bottoms and such like, and the *Hatchet* stake F is used for truing up or forming nearly any turned-over edge either for box bottoms and lids or for wiring such straight edges as may enter into the construction.

The *Half-moon* stake L serves a similar purpose for circular work and is usually about 4 in. across its diameter.

The *Funnel* stake is, as its name indicates, for working up conical formations ; the little " extinguisher " stake, J, was designed for a similar purpose, for rounding up extinguishers when our grandparents and others farther back went to bed with candlesticks. They just reached over the bed, one supposes, and popped a wee conical hat over the candle to effect a black-out. Yes,—even special tools to make extinguishers still come in handy for other but similar work in these modern times.

The *Bick* or *Beak Iron* shown at I is a lean looking anvil with multitudes of uses which range from the forming of funnel spouts to the finishing of work begun on the hatchet stake. The lengths vary, beaks being from about 10 in. long to about 20 in. in the large sizes when they weigh about forty pounds and more.

The *Pipe Stake*, K, will round up any circular body either for a tea-caddy or a chimney for a stove or a rainwater chute. Lengths of horns vary from about 18 in. to 30 in. and weigh up to round seventy pounds in the large size. H shows a *Creasing* stake which may be used for working up beads on flat work for ornamental purposes or for strengthening, say, a box side, or it may be used to finish off a wired edge either on flat or circular work, as well as starting off a crease to receive a wire.

The *Bench-Bar* or *Mandrel* M is one of the handiest tools in a sheet-metalworker's kit. Over-hung and clipped to the bench as in G, Fig. 15, it may be used for rounding up and seaming any cylindrical or box-shaped forms. Round, oval or rectangular tanks may be seamed and/or riveted upon its faces. The square hole in the flat end will house any of the stakes or heads shown above it ; again, it will take jennies, wiring machines or swages and may be used as a base for cutting metal with cold-chisel, provided some other metal is interposed to take the chisel edge during the process. There are various short stakes or dwarf heads that can be had to fit these bars, but nothing need be said of these now. Fig. 7 will cover most jobs. There are quite a number of jobs which will crop up from time to time where gadgets will perform the desired operation better, in my experience, than hand tools of the orthodox type.

Special small handy *folders* are made similarly to Fig. 2, and are just a couple of lengths of bright drawn (or even black, if it comes to that) mild steel with a pair or two pairs

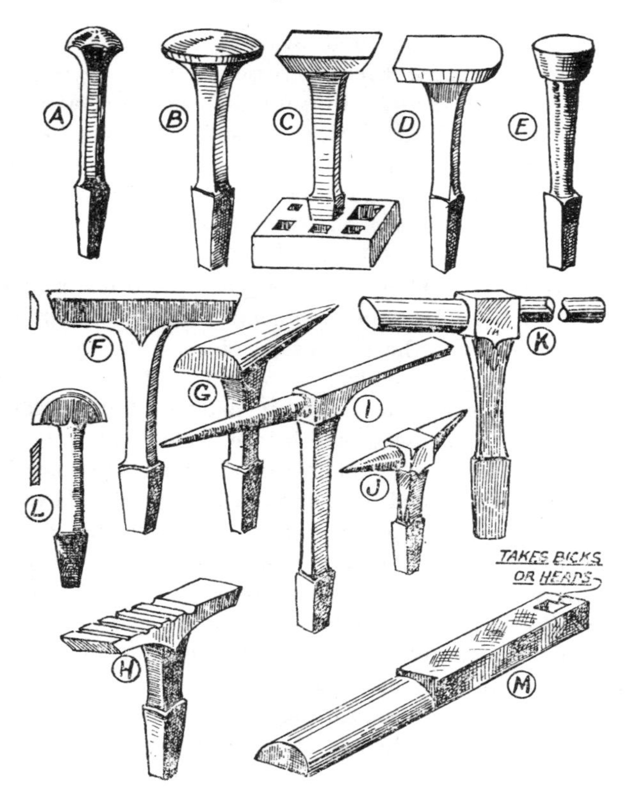

(a) Pepper box stake, (b) dome-head, (c) pan-head, (d) kettle-bottom, (e) canister, (f) hatchet, (g) funnel, (h) creasing, (i) bick iron, (j) extinguisher stake, (k) pipe, (l) half-moon, (m) bench-bar or mandrel (sizes from about 2½ in. × 30 in. to 4 in. × 48 in.).

Fig. 7.—Stakes

of draw-bolt holes at suitable centre distances apart to accommodate any desired width of metal. Gripping the tang end in the vice, the work is clamped between bars with the " bending line " just visible, and the part to be bent or folded is then knocked over with a mallet, and if desired, finished off with a light hammer. Make these up as required for various jobs. Some may have square edges and others may be chamfered off along the top (see Fig. 2). For edging bottoms or tops of vessels, either square, oval, round, hexagonal or any odd shape which may have to be repeated to pretty close limits, cut a hard-wood block to such a shape very slightly smaller than the inside dimension required and use as in Figs. 12, H. and I, (discs) for edging over. Going all the way on the job, have them cast off a wooden pattern allowing about 1/16 for shrinkage of metal and then file up to shape. I have a score or so of such former plates on which literally hundreds of such small ends and covers have been hammered up, the advantage of these being that the product is unvarying in size.

Besides such things as "former plates," I use "former rings" similar to those shown in the sketch. The purpose of these is for edging a concave or convex (depends which way one looks at it) end for a tank or drum. Placed saucer-like on the ring, the protruding edge is knocked over all round, thus making the use of a jenny unnecessary; to throw off such an edge by means of a stake would be next to impossible because of the curvature of the end—and, again, the results are uniform. Then there are blocking out or hollowing plates made in metal—mainly cast iron—on which various small hollowed forms may be hammered out with dispatch and a fair degree of accuracy. These also are shown in sketch.

The machine tools, if such they may be called, are almost as numerous as those for hand operation, but for the purpose of the small shop, mention will be made of a few more or less essential ones.

Jennies

These tools are pretty familiar in most shops. As shown in Fig. 16, they are made to fit a bench hole or to fit into a socket in a bench mandrel, or again, they may be clamped in a big vice.

Mainly designed for *edging*, that particular type can,

in understanding and persuasive hands, be made to perform the complete wiring operation, a certain amount of light swaging and to tighten a loose disc which has been wired. Straight-sided work can also be " wangled " through it as long as the work can be conveniently held and/or supported. It may not be strictly correct, but I put wiring machines into the jenny class, calling them *edging* and *wiring* jennies. The wiring machine is very similar to the jenny proper, with the difference that it has interchangeable wheels for effecting the turn-over action for reception of the wire, and in some machines a special wheel for tucking in the edge of the metal over the wire.

Then comes the *Swaging* machine, which puts fancy and plain grooves round both circular, straight, and/or cylindrical forms, the purpose for such operations being in some cases purely decorative and in others for strength with the " decorative " idea still in view, and yet again, for the support of inset bottoms and tops prior to seaming or edging over.

The *Rolling Machine* is fairly essential, although I have never owned one and manage to get along well enough. If, however, it became necessary to cover all classes of sheet metal work as a full time job, instead of just as an adjunct to a small general engineering business, the possession of such rollers would become imperative.

Stove pipes, binnacle-stand pillars, tanks, oil-drums, in fact, anything longer than, say, six inches, may be more conveniently and quickly rolled into circularity by this means than by any amount of skilled wangling by hand over a bench stake or mandrel or bench bar.

CHAPTER II

THE METALS USED

THE most generally used metals which the small shop will have to deal with may be fairly safely predicted. Brass, copper and aluminium will cover most of the work going through, with the exception of tinned plate, usually known as " tinplate " but which is actually steel. The tinplate may be the general material in a tinsmith's shop, where the presence of non-ferrous sheets is rare, but the latter come more truly under the generally accepted sense of " sheet-metal " working, as distinct from tinsmith's work. This must not be taken in a derogatory sense—far be it from me to detract from the skill of the tinsmith, whose art in persuading such intractable stuff as " tin " to be wired, blocked, seamed and otherwise worked, is really something to be proud of—but my metal working has been mainly confined to the non-ferrous variety, possibly making use of some unorthodox methods due to circumstances prevailing, hence my desire to pass on hints that may be of use to others similarly situated.

Brass

Sheet brass is a very tractable metal (or alloy, to be exact) and apart from its pleasing appearance when polished, has quite a number of qualities to recommend it. It certainly will not rust ; it is fairly proof against sea air, hence its use in the manufacture of ships' compasses, binnacles, lamps, bridge instruments and so on ; it is non-magnetic, of course. It can be satisfactorily made up into tanks for petrol, paraffin and crude oil, and is not unduly affected by them. To make doubly sure, however, I have made a practice of using tinned sheet brass for this latter purpose.

For domestic purposes, brass sheet may be usefully and artistically applied to trays, fire screens, electric porch or hall lanterns, fireplace curbs, coal boxes and a host of other things, though the present day tendency for easy housekeeping seems to have banished a lot of the old-time pleasant looking sheet metalware from our homes, leaving us to gaze upon the frigid glare of chromium—chromium and still more chromium. We now even sit on chromium chairs and eat off chromium plates laid on chromium tables, and some of us will doubtless die in chromium beds. Anyway, we see little of the old cheerful brass-ware as in days gone by, but now and then someone desires to have something made up of brass and that offers a chance for the sheet metalworker to keep his hand in the old trade.

Many of the old sheet metal artifices are lost to us, but most of the hand working methods are the fruits of experiments tried out in far off Biblical days, when there was much talk of images of brass, gates of brass, and so on. That " brass " was most probably " bronze " but it was yellow anyway, and to most laymen anything that they definitely know is not gold but looks yellow, is just " brass."

Copper

Copper is actually more ductile than brass, and may be worked up into practically any form. It has a great affinity for solder, even more so than brass, in my opinion, though they are both " good solderers." My experience in connection with copper shows that salt atmosphere has a more deleterious effect upon it than upon brass. Anyway, one rarely sees ship's fittings of copper. Paraffin oil, in some circumstances which the author cannot exactly trace or understand, absolutely eats copper away. Large thirty and fifty gallon tanks have eaten out inside a couple of years. Cut up for scrap, the insides revealed a thick coating of black skin-like stuff adhering to the sheet metal all over ; whilst the bottom surface was more or less riddled with pinholes, or where not absolutely through, showed pits which could be picked through with a scriber. One dare not scrape in preparation for a solder repair or the lot would collapse. The same trouble has never yet occurred with sheet brass however; evidently a problem for the metallurgist.

Used artistically, copper has a very warm cheerful appearance, and was formerly greatly in demand for household metal goods. Trays, fireplace furniture, lamps, etc., copper kitchen pots (tinned with sal-ammoniac) were the rule in most big establishments, though now the use of aluminium and rustless steel has ousted most copper utensils from the domestic regions. The repairer, however, may still get a job or two now and then to reproduce some antique or other, a copper coal box, or a curb for the fireplace, or even a real copper kettle.

It may not be generally known that copper is peculiarly affected by contact with carbide or the acetylene gas generated therefrom.

Some years ago, quite a number of my clients evinced a desire to have small generators for this gas made up from copper sheet. The idea was that copper was "everlasting." Quite unthinkingly, and in the best of faith, these were made up, and the customers highly satisfied—for a while. Came a day when one customer, looking rather upset, entered the shop bearing the badly battered remains of a container.

Explanation revealed that after quite satisfactory use for a while, on that particular day the water container had been removed to replenish the carbide in the vessel below, and that such removal had permitted the water vessel to just scrape the side of the main can in so doing. Result—can, water container and the owner were mixed up in quite a sizable explosion. The can whizzed past the man's head by a very narrow margin, hit the underside of the deck (otherwise, the cabin ceiling of the boat it was used on) and rebounded. Such was the force of the explosion that the container was squashed in like a concertina, whilst the main container, some fifteen inches high by ten inches diameter was split right down the side—20 gauge sheet too.

Shortly after this affair, came another, though not quite so spectacular, which upon enquiry seemed due to a similar cause—the water container either scraped or hit the side of the main vessel during removal. The action was in fact, practically on par with striking a match on the side of the box. The copper, after a certain degree of use, had, one supposes, absorbed certain properties present in the carbide or the resultant gas, which caused the metal to strike fire whenever friction or impact took place. Upon trying to knock some of the bulges out, every time the metal was struck with a hammer there was another flash and a crack, smoke and a rotten smell. Copper pipe for the gas is also affected in like manner—chokes up very quickly, eats itself away, and if one attempts to clear it, shoots out fire like a squib.

The illustrations on the next two pages show all that was left of a brass generator after explosion during the soldering of the little " drip " nipple, seen at the top (which is actually the " bottom " in use). No blow-lamp was used anywhere near it. The soldering iron was only half-hot and the precaution had been taken to scratch-brush off any incandescent particles of soot adhering thereto. The work was three parts completed when there was a flash—a terrific bang and the whole outfit flew past my head.

You can see the state the thing is in. The split paned-down and sweated seam is cut clean through. Note the split where the edge pulled out straight, and the split on the edge of the tapered end. The cross-bar measures somewhere round 10 in. × 1½ in. wide and ⅜ in. thick. The container—kept as a souvenir—is of twenty gauge brass. Repairs were out of the question, but it was decided to reclaim the cross-bar and nipple. The job was photographed and next day a blowlamp was tentatively played upon the nipple to unsolder it. As soon as the heat got at it, the thing went off banging again, little ones this time, but none the less "bangs." The moral seems to be: avoid soldering any generator water drip or carbide can unless it is guaranteed to have been unused and in the open air, for—well, at least fifty years.

Result of soldering, with "iron" only, the drip nipple on brass water container of acetylene generator. Note split on top seam (actually the bottom of generator)

This was the first brass one that has ever done this trick, and, by the way, the filler plug was out, too. Should I ever make a new one complete, either lead coated brass sheet would be used, or else ordinary heavily tinned brass. Up to the moment of writing this, ordinary "galvanised" ones have caused no trouble. For a safe rule: use ferrous metals if at all possible.

Aluminium has, in recent years, become a great favourite in domestic circles. Very convenient for kettles, saucepans, frying pans, etc. . . . . until the rivets pull through and the handles drop off, or perhaps, a wee pinhole appears in the side or bottom. Unlike our friendly old brass and copper, it is impossible to solder such a job by using the ordinary solder or methods. There are hosts of proprietory aluminium solders on the market, but these require methods of application very different from the general soldering procedure for other metals. The main features which recommend aluminium to the worker are its extreme ductility in the

Top of generator, showing 1½ in. × 4¾ in. clamp bar. Note paned down and sweated seam torn through, and torn (20 s.w.g. brass) body

usual qualities, and the ease with which it may be cut. Salt atmosphere, however, causes it to turn a nasty grey colour, roughen up and generally lose its ductility to the extent of becoming brittle. It will, in certain circumstances, even disintegrate, thus rendering it of but little use for marine fittings from the standpoint of permanency.

Galvanised sheet, very often wrongly called "iron" is steel, and in the heavier gauges which may be called "plate" it is very pleasant stuff to work—ductile to a great degree, it can be intricately bent (or even abused) before fracture takes place. Cisterns and tanks may be made up from this plate, manhole covers or inspection doors may also be made from it, in fact, anything in the way of sheet work in the engineering line may with advantage be fabricated from this galvanised sheet or plate.

To solder, it is necessary to use spirits of salts in order to get a really sound joint and to scrape the galvanised coating off where the join occurs, afterwards thoroughly washing off in clean water and drying. Where permissible, it is my practice to scrub in paraffin as a deterrent against subsequent rusting. To make a good job of cutting such sheets in the absence of adequate shearing appliances, sheet metal cutting hack-saws are ideal. Once a sheet, especially the thicker ones round 1/16 in. and $\frac{1}{8}$ in., is buckled in cutting, it takes quite a bit of truing up, so it is better to take a little longer and saw to size when working from a big sheet which may be six feet long by two or three in width.

CHAPTER III

HOLLOWING AND BLOCKING

BEFORE either of these two processes can be performed a hollowing block is necessary. This is simply a block or log of wood of such height that it comes about knee high if used when seated on a stool, or just about waist high if the user stands up to do his hollowing. It is a matter which the worker will decide for himself, though actually the available size of log at the time of fitting out may decide for him.

The hollows in the block may be gouged out, those in the top of the block being, say, about six, four, and two inches in diameter, by approximately two, one, and say, a half an inch in depth respectively. The actual contours of these hollows need not be truly hemispherical as the user may wish to incorporate a number of merging curvatures into each hollow, and by practice can then hollow and block any number of different hollowed forms on the same block, some being of flattish bottom form with steeply blocked, but possibly shallow sides, and so on.

The bottom end of block may have a larger hollow in it more or less true in contour for finishing or final blocking of the larger bowls. The hollow bottom also gives a firmer standing effect to the block. A wobbly block is very aggravating.

So much for the shape. Now for the wood, which should be dry and as free from " shakes " or splits as possible. Elm is as good as anything. Beech is very good, too, if it can be obtained. Should it evince a tendency to split, get a smith to make and shrink on a hoop, top and bottom, as is done on cart wheel hubs.

The procedure is shown in Fig. 8. Having cut the disc to the requisite size, a matter which will be discussed later on, seat yourself or stand comfortably in front of the block, and, holding the disc between fingers and thumb—thumb facing you—rub the hammer loosely, but controllably held, once firmly across from centre to edge ; this will mark a starting radius line from which to begin the rings of blows. Begin at about $\frac{3}{8}$ in. from the edge, and using a free style of blow, elbow to side and working wrist and forearm only, proceed to work the disc anti-clockwise with the left hand. Rotate so that the disc moves at a nice even rate under and between the hammer blows. Time the movement of the left hand so that the disc moves when the hammer is going up. Some people begin to work with nerves and muscles "keyed up to the nines" and gripping the hammer till their knuckles nearly burst the skin. You will soon get tired that way. Try to cultivate a sort of lackadaisical style. Do not expend too much energy in lifting the hammer, nor bang it down hard—this jars the nerves and muscles, and if, say, four to eight hours' work at the block is likely (and I have done it often enough) it pays to avoid tiring. A good "stylist" just raises the hammer with a flick of the wrist, helped by a certain amount of "bounce" left over from the previous blow and to all appearances just as indifferently lets it fall again. There is no "indifference" in the act though. Every blow is uniform, timed to a nicety—sixty to sixty-five a minute, and a good hammer man can do an eight inch bowl clear of the finish blocking at one spell of hammering. Don't try to emulate this for a start or the forearm muscles will tie up and a pain come in the elbow joint. Cultivate the easy going style and there will be little "hammer elbow" to get scared of.

Having gone round one ring of blows and come back to

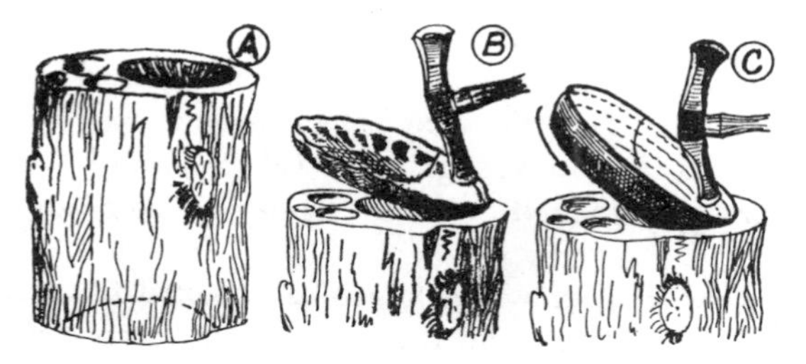

A typical block

Start about ½ in. from edge and work inwards

Ease out crinkles and carry on in circles

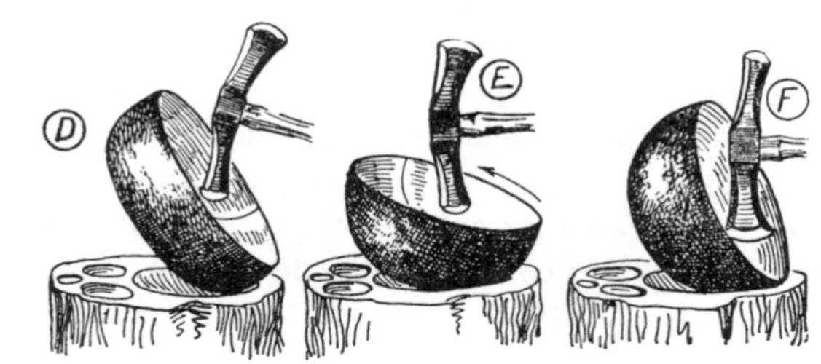

Raise the angle and hit square

Work the bottom right in to centre

Change ends with hammer and block all over again to final shape

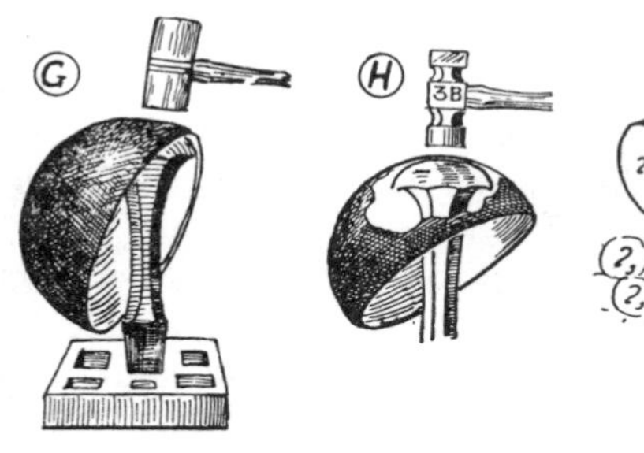

Work all over with mallet, using domed stake

Repeat previous operation, using flat faced hammer rubbed clean on emery cloth

Unless hammer is clean every little dust particle on it will be shown with each blow

Fig. 8.—Hollowing and blocking

the line scratched by the hammer poll at the outset, begin the next ring just touching the edge of the last row and carry on as before. By the time the second ring is done the result will be near enough to sketch 8B, and by the time the centre is reached will be showing something like sketch C.

The diameter at the edge must be checked from time to time. If it is closing in on the size desired, give it a ring of blows right on the edge to stretch it, and if it is still too big give it an extra series where the start was made—three-eighths of an inch in from the edge, before starting the next series inwards towards the centre. At certain stages of the hollowing, creases will appear in the bowl, which, if left therein, will produce cracks, so these must be gently persuaded to smooth themselves out as the job proceeds.

It may be noticed that the metal becomes harder as one proceeds deeper. If such hardness does occur, for copper, heat up uniformly to blood red and quench in cold water; for brass, heat up to a darker red and let cool off on its own, after which either will be found to be quite tractable again. Then proceed toward the final hollowing stage shown at E. When depth and diameter suit requirements, change over to the blocking hammer F., which has a curvature slightly less than that of the bowl. Turn the block end up and carry on smoothing the unevenly hollowed bowl into the more uniformly made hollow, being careful to strike fair and not leave any "half moons" from the hammer edge. Also keep an eye on the diameter so that it does not vary from requirements or circularity. There should be little difficulty in keeping within a sixteenth of an inch of round, and with two similar bowls, when placed face to face, their edges should coincide. Impossible to do by hand, you may be told. On the contrary, with practice it can be done any time, though it must be admitted that no two workers obtain exactly similar results. One may stretch his metal more than the other.

You may be able to get a bowl from a sheet or disc of metal very little bigger than the finished size of bowl ; it comes out of the thickness. Some workers stretch the bottoms more than the edges, getting thin bottoms. Others, again in the initial stages, take it out of the edges and finally have a moderately thick bottom. The worker (from my experience) will not know for quite a while whether he has a uniform result or not. The only way he can tell is by feeling with finger and thumb all over the surface, a procedure which calls for a certain degree of "knack," and by that word it is intended to convey something which "comes" and which cannot be taught. One can see how the metal is distributed during subsequent operations which entail cutting into the sides or bottom or drilling for rivets, etc. The respective thicknesses may then be seen and compared and one knows more or less the results and trend of one's hollowing procedure. If you go too thin, the bowl bottom or side (wherever the ultra thinness happens to be) will show a nice little split when held to the light. Such a split it may be possible to eliminate in later stages if any cutting agrees with the position of such a crack. If not, you can almost assuredly scrap the job, begin another and "be canny wi' the hammer" next time.

After the bowl has been satisfactorily blocked out, the job can be further improved by closing the, by this time, rather porous-looking outer surface of the metal caused by that surface having been stretched.

A large dome-head stake (Fig. 7B) is fitted into a convenient bench hole or into an iron socket, or else gripped in a large vice, and the bowl, while being moved round and about on this, is firmly hammered with a flat-faced planishing hammer (Fig. 3B), of about ½ lb. or ¾ lb. in weight.

Be sure the bowl sits fair on the curved bead of the stake because, failing this precaution, the blows, instead of further truing up the shape, will only bulge or distort it. You can easily locate the work on the stake fairly by balancing it in any position of its surface and pressing it into contact with the face of the hammer. At the " lie " so obtained, proceed with the hammering, keeping it so that the blows sound nice and firm as well as feel so. Use will soon put you wise to this. Go all over the job and be careful that the hammer and stake faces are perfectly clean.

Dust and Grease

A hair or a large grain of dusty matter (Fig. 8I) adhering to the hammer face will reproduce that same shaped indent where every blow is struck, and if a polished surface is subsequently desired, hundreds of such little marks will take quite a lot of abrasive and mop polishing to remove entirely. Another thing to remember is that before this planishing, the hammer face should be rubbed on á sheet of blue-back emery cloth resting on something flat, such as a smooth block of wood or metal ; *e.g.*, the surface plate used for flat planishing. Push the hammer to and fro on the emery in prolongation with the handle and the surface of the head will show a linear ground face.

When hammering up the bowl, wipe it free of all grease which may adhere thereto, and which comes mainly from handling. Having done this, it will be seen upon commencing to hammer that the hammer marks are very distinct, though not indented or " feelable," this visibility showing definitely where the hammering has been done and where, if at all, it has been missed. As hammering proceeds, these marks will become less distinct and upon looking at the hammer face a dirty greasy mark will be seen in the middle. Wipe this off, either on a rag or on the bench surface. Too much emery cloth only grinds back the hardness of the hammer face, though one supposes there is enough " hammer " present to last a good few years, even if rubbed ultra frequently.

Having once wiped the job it may be wondered where this other grease comes from. I believe it exudes from the metal in process of closing the pores thereof, added to by that from the hands during rotation of the work.

From time to time, arguments have cropped up as to whether the method of hollowing herein described is correct. Some have maintained that their own particular way is to " stick the work on a hollow block and bump it in the middle."

For shallow (and very shallow at that) saucer like forms, such a procedure may be as good as any other, but for a bowl as shown here the bang-it-in-the-middle method is simply asking for failure. Proof of a pudding is eating it. Work a bowl as already described, and then try another one and bump it in the middle and work outwards. In the initial stages of the second " method " the " bumper " will obtain something very like a half-opened umbrella—radiating crinkles all over, each crinkle coming back as quickly as it is removed and each crinkle being a potential crack.

Raising

Hollowing and blocking are not, however, the only means of producing a hollow form such as a saucer or bowl.

There is an operation known as Raising. This is done directly on the stake and the worker begins *in the middle* and works outwards, the tendency being in this case to thin the metal towards the outer edges, while keeping it fairly thick centrally—just the exact opposite to the foregoing process. It is a method, moreover, which is not greatly in favour. but a few words may usefully be said concerning it.

The disc of metal—copper, brass or aluminium—is placed centrally over the dome headed stake and then worked down over it, using a hard-wood mallet or a hammer, an operation which is more akin to " drawing " the metal than anything else. The sheet is induced to " flow " and in so doing the metal round the middle portions remains more or less of the original thickness, while that at the sides becomes thinner. During this process, as well as in the hollowing previously described, wrinkles will occur and these must be smoothed out or cracks will result and ruin the job.

Some workers deliberately wrinkle a disc that is to be blocked out, doubtless in order to reduce a certain amount of side pull on the metal during the initial stages of hollowing. Be that as it may, hollowed forms such as described, from three to ten inches diameter, having depths round about the forty per cent. diameter mark, can be produced, without anything that can honestly be described as a " wrinkle "—and this on metal sheet not exceeding twenty gauge.

The cause of this tendency to wrinkle is that in the disc of metal destined to become a bowl there is a neutral zone between the centre and edge which has no expansion or contraction to speak of. Being in the one sheet, however, the domed part of the bowl can expand, though not as regards actual diameter. It forms the domed surface. The increased area is there but is bounded by the non-increasing neutral zone ; as it cannot move sideways it moves upwards into a curve. Now on the other side of this neutral zone is another ; and this, being integral, of course, is held from expansion by the adjacent metal in that neutral zone. The free edge of the embryo bowl is also neutral, as the actual hollowing blows begin some third of an inch inwards from that. Hammering causes expansion, but expansion is restricted by the neutral zone and by the unhammered edge , it therefore becomes " loose " and forms wrinkles.

Cutting the Disc

Discs may be cut to size in a number of ways, but it is intended to show only the simplest and, therefore, most applicable to a " small " shop. This is the purely graphical method, and subject to the fact (as are all these methods of disc cutting) that one worker can produce from a certain size blank deeper work than another, no difficulties should arise.

The main object is never to cut too small: you can always resort to the snips and trim off a little if it looks as if the job is not coming the proper size.

In Fig. 9A is a bowl of a certain diameter and depth. Set off such a depth as denoted by **x**, **y** along a vertical line. From the point **x** and at right angles to it, produce **x z**.

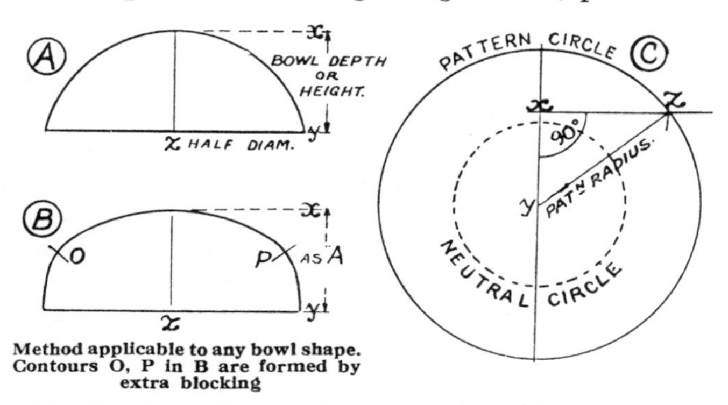

Method applicable to any bowl shape. Contours O, P in B are formed by extra blocking

Fig. 9.—Preparing bowl patterns (graphical method)

This x z represents the half-diameter of the desired bowl. Join y, z and that hypoteneuse represents the radius for the cutting size.

Midway, theoretically, is a " neutral circle " around which the metal neither expands or contracts during working, a fact depending on the technique of the worker. To produce such a bowl as Fig. 9B, just do a little extra blocking and study the shape as you proceed. As a rough guide, try such sizes as these: $8\frac{1}{2}$ in. blocks to $7\frac{1}{2}$ in. or $7\frac{5}{8}$ in.; 7 in. blocks 6 in. or $6\frac{1}{8}$ in.; $5\frac{1}{4}$ in. blocks to $4\frac{1}{2}$ in., and so on. Just practice. Remember to provide wiring or flanging allowances.

CHAPTER IV

FLANGING

VERY few examples of sheet metal work do not have to be flanged at some point in their construction. If a can be made up the body has to be flanged at the bottom before one can fit and seam and knock-up the edge.

Should a stove-pipe be made the oblique joint at the elbow must be flanged before it may be joined. Flanging is often used as a jointing method of joining a couple of pipes end to end. The start-off for a hand-wired body is also a flange and although some are comparatively narrow flanges on fairly large diameters, in other cases the flanges may be quite wide in relation to the diameter of the tube operated upon.

The process is similar to Fig. 10, A, B, C, D. Very often done in its initial stages on a " Hatchet " stake, Fig. 7F, it may be more conveniently carried out on the slightly rounded edge of a " Creasing " stake, 7H, a small bench anvil, or plain square bar held in the vice or even a " Bick," Fig. 7I. Begin as in B, with the cylinder nearly flat on the stake face. With a bossing mallet or a hammer, if skilled in the *gentle* use of that tool, work around the mouth of the vessel, rolling the cylinder along the stake towards operator with the left hand in such a way as to produce a ring on the outer edge denoting the depth of flange. This ring, although visible on the inner side of metal, is still not deep. Next, lower the left hand and bring the next flanging further over as in C, using the mallet this time, and then again further until stage D is reached, when the job may be finished off with the flat-

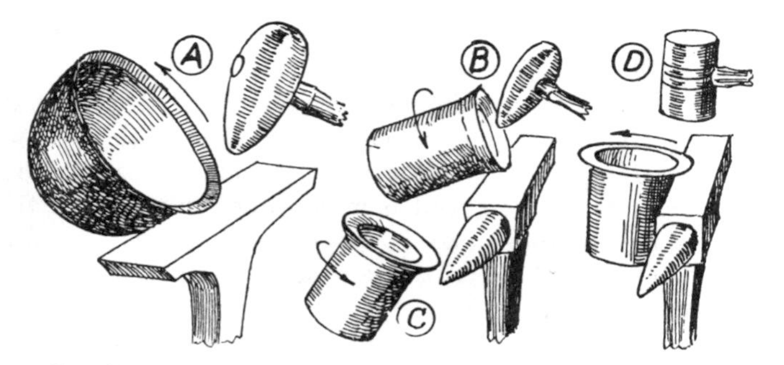

For either bowl or cylindrical work grip where most comfortably controlled, rotate anti-clockwise. Start as " A," continue as " B " and proceed by about four stages to " D," when the flange may be finished by mallet or flat hammer

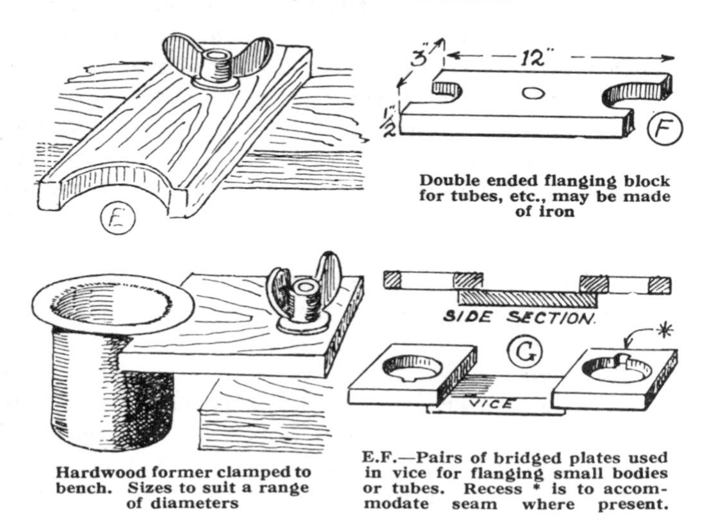

Double ended flanging block for tubes, etc., may be made of iron

Hardwood former clamped to bench. Sizes to suit a range of diameters

E.F.—Pairs of bridged plates used in vice for flanging small bodies or tubes. Recess * is to accommodate seam where present.

Fig. 10.—Hand flanging or edging

faced hammer. Should the length of such a job preclude its being held as shown, it may be worked in a horizontal position, the flanging being done on the side face of the anvil or stake. The flanging of nearly every form is by the same method, and using due care not to cut the metal in the initial stage the operation is what may be termed "plain sailing." Be careful not to rush the job, however, or splits may occur which, in certain cases, will ruin it. Although the operations are shown as A to D there is no valid reason why an operator must confine himself to just that four. He can go round as many times and as gradually as his skill demands, and it may be said that "making haste slowly" is as good a motto as any when applied to this type of work.

Two other very handy accessories, the use of which will enable more accurate flanging to be done, are shown in Fig. 10 E and F, and also at G. G features a section on side elevation, and the gadget is made of a couple of square or rectangular iron or steel plates about four inches dimension either way. In these are bored holes of such diameter as will suit any particular size of job necessitating a certain degree of dispatch in production of the flanges. At one side of the hole in each plate a clearance slot is filed to take the seamed joint if necessary. To these squares is welded a cross bar of fair section, the ends just coming short of the holes in the plates. This bar is held in the vice and the work passed through until the requisite amount for flanging stands proud of the top face, when with bossing mallet or round-faced hammer, the flange is gently worked or "thrown off." The upper edges of these holes may be rounded off to suit any degree of "fillet" or radius for flanging that may be desired. In any case it is advisable to remove to about a thirty-second of an inch radius so that there is less likelihood of the edge cutting the metal if used in unthinking hands.

These plates may also be made open-sided or U-shaped to facilitate possible removal of a double-flanged tube, and a larger type of this pattern is shown in F, Fig. 10.

Made of hard-wood—oak, ash, beech, or any such similar material—they are eminently suitable for the production of flanges on work four inches diameter or over (Fig 10E).

They may be secured overhanging the bench by means of a large bolt and wing-nut or by a metal or wood strap or " strong-backs " and a couple of bolts and nuts or wing nuts.

There is no reason, either, to conform to true circularity, as they may be made also in sets of such varying contour as will enable flanges to be thrown off ovals and even off rounded corners of less radius than 10E. These latter, I found handy for beginning the wired edge of rectangular

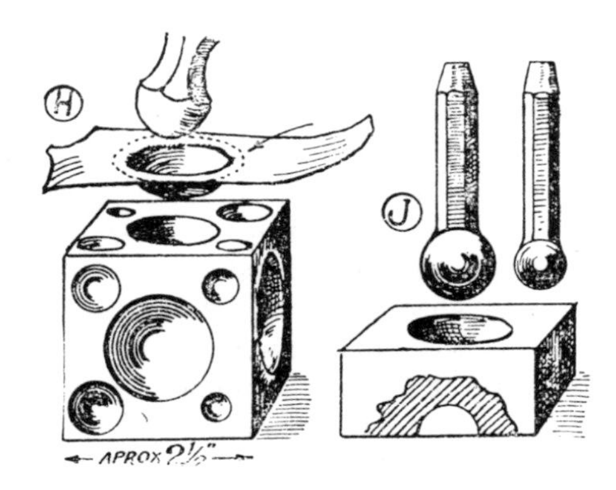

Doming block.—Block first, then trim off waste as shown

Stud boss and pair of punches

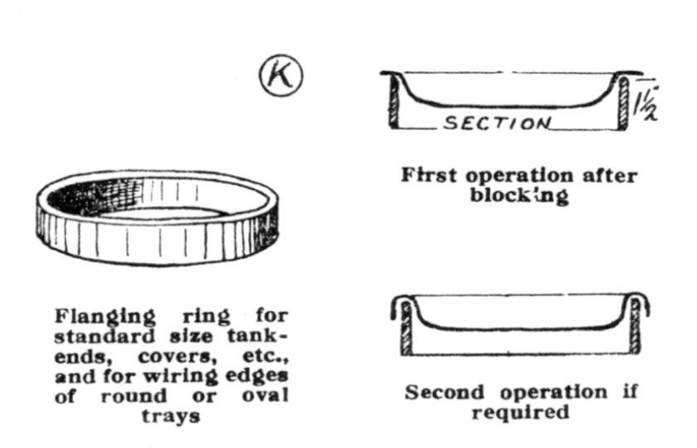

Flanging ring for standard size tank-ends, covers, etc., and for wiring edges of round or oval trays

First operation after blocking

Second operation if required

Fig. 10a.—Items of kit

copper and brass trays having rounded blocked corners of about inch and a half radius.

In Fig. 10aH is a steel block, in the sides of which are machined out a number of hemispherical cavities, ranging from about 2 in. Actually, the one in use has never been measured, but it is round the 2 in. diameter, down to about $\frac{1}{4}$ in. On this block, as may be seen, various sizes of cups or "studs" may be domed up; these are used on can bottoms, etc., to minimise wear and to prevent rusty bottoms; also for small lids and so on. Any scrap piece may be used. Place on block and hold down primarily between extended finger and thumb, and hit between with the ball of the hammer or with the bossing mallet. If the edges rise slightly in the process, knock back and flatten with flat mallet. The piece will eventually locate itself, when the operation may be completed. Then trim off the surplus and that's that. The stud boss and punches at J do a like job and further comment is unnecessary.

The flanging ring K may be made circular, oval, or rectangular (with radiused corners, say $1\frac{1}{2}$ or 2 in.) over which the edges of tank ends, covers or trays may be flanged as shown in first operation or knocked over to take a wire as in the second operation. As so done, I fit this type of end into tanks, dome outwards, solder in place 3/16 in. inwards from tank edge, turn that edge in over the turned edge of end, and again solder. These rings may be of any size. They are welded of iron to suit the wiring, and one stows inside the other.

CHAPTER V

EDGING AND SEAMING

In the working up of a given job, allowances for the various joints must be made. Patterns used for repetition work in the small jobbing shop are usually cut from tinned plate though sometimes, in a hurry, brown paper is used and a metal one cut afterwards. They should all have the extra seaming and edging or wiring allowances added at the time of cutting out as otherwise you may forget that these pieces have to be joined together, with the result that upon trying to do so they will be too small . . . more scrap metal in the box. So see that all such allowances are scribed upon the pattern first and cut carefully to that size. The more carefully these are cut the greater will be the ease of assembly, and the neater the finished job. Nothing looks worse than a seam all out of square with the body lines of a can or other cylindrical or square object.

Certain work, as for example the bottom of a " peined " can, must have a double allowance put on all round. Supposing now a can to be 4 in. diameter with a $\frac{1}{8}$ in. flanged bottom. When the body is edged over on the stake or in the jenny it will be $4\frac{1}{4}$ in. diameter. Over this a bottom has to be fitted—edged over and peined down tight, when, if neatly done, the edge peined over will just about touch the can body all round. In order to do this there must be sufficient metal allowed over the flanged diameter plus 1/32 in. for the bend, which brings the size of the bottom to $4\frac{1}{4}$ in., plus twice 5/32 in. (the margin round) or a total of 4 9/16 in. But this has to be *bent up* over the edged bottom, a simple enough operation but one that will steal a little of our marginal metal, and leave the resultant peined on bottom well clear of the can body. It matters not the least as long as it is tight, but it does not look nice. True enough one can file off a little all round the bottom flange, and with luck, pein in tight to the can sides and so gain a little, but actually one should allow about a couple of metal thicknesses extra on the cutting size for the bottom which will bring that 4 9/16 in. to about a bare $4\frac{5}{8}$ in. Place the flanged bottom fair in the middle of the flat disc, look it over and make sure the can body is pretty round, scribe around the flange on to the disc and with either the jenny or hand methods throw off the edge to give a nice easy fit on the bottom of the can.

Similarly with seaming; the grooved or "hooked" joint requires an allowance of three times the width of seam—plus that same little extra for bending and setting-in the seam. This amount depends much, both in this and the previous case, upon the skill of the operator. Some can work up a joint with the metal cut pretty bare, others need full measure in order to do a good job. It is different from fitting and turning, where a "thou" is a "thou," and where either a job fits or else it does not. In sheet metal working a good man can stretch a scanty body or a flanged edge and make it fit. A length of metal cut short can be made to grow so that it *still* has to be trimmed down to fit. The hammer is a very handy tool—used properly.

In Fig. 11 is shown the construction of an outside and an inside seam. Nearly every canister, bucket, oil drum, or small tank is joined longitudinally by this method. Buckets are mostly seamed and galvanised right away, without any soldering, though buckets have been brought to me from a hardware store to be soldered along that particular seam.

A glance at the sketches "a" to "d" in this figure will make constructional details clear. Note the couple of opposite hooks in "b" and how the top edge is set-in where the arrow points in "a."

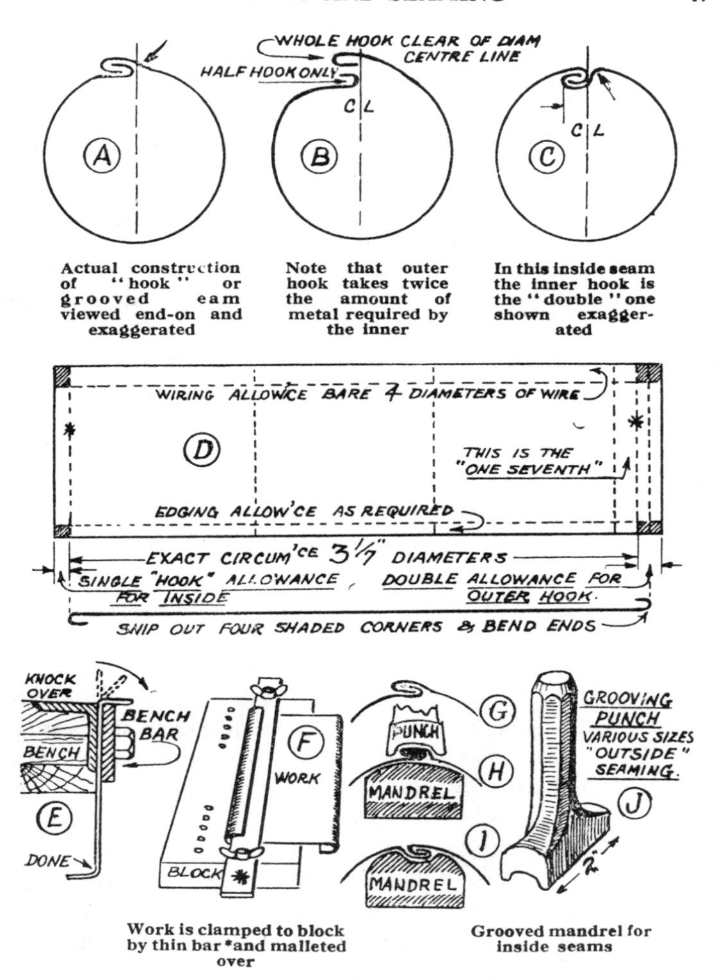

Actual construction of "hook" or grooved eam viewed end-on and exaggerated

Note that outer hook takes twice the amount of metal required by the inner

In this inside seam the inner hook is the "double" one shown exaggerated

Work is clamped to block by thin bar *and malleted over

Grooved mandrel for inside seams

Fig. 11.—Side seaming

This operation is done as sketch H for outside seam by means of a grooving punch as shown, though I use one considerably less in groove length than the commercial type shown. A groove length of 1 in. seems plenty, and is made from a piece of 1 in. × ½ in. tool steel cut about 4 in. long, grooved with the file and left untempered. One of these has lasted ten years. In the same illustration, " d " shows how to cut for wiring, edging and seaming allowances. Some may wire a job tighter than others, but for safety's sake you can allow a bare 4 wire diameters for wiring allowance at the top of a job. To get this easily, cut off a ½ in. strip of the metal being used and bend it round a piece of the wire, using pliers, and after scribing where the bend touches the straight, unbend it and measure the scribed distance. That is your wiring allowance for a tightly wired job. You can add, say, 1/64 in. to this.

Next, mark along the lower edge where the work has to be flanged or edged to take the can bottom disc or plate, and where this and the wiring line intersect the seaming lines, cut away the little rectangular pieces shown shaded in sketch " d " as if this is overlooked, it will be impossible to wire or edge top or bottom afterwards. The two inner vertical lines * * represent near enough the circumference of the body inside, but in bending the " hooks," see that the bend comes on the second line of the double allowance side and bend this

Old Cornish "tin" pitcher

Actually an example of conical work in copper. Joined with " edge " and paned-down seams. Side seams grooved with groove inside. Neck wired and lap seamed, fitted in place and handle secured before bottom half paned down and fixed. Handle wired and jennied on " face " edges. Bottom blocked. Hole cut small and hammered into shape on stake

inwards; the single allowance at the other side of strip is bent outwards. Be careful about this. One may easily make a mistake and bend a pair alike, or

Examples of plain, square and cylindrical work before assembly. Tinned before working up (as Fig. 33). Lap (ornamental edge) seamed, edged and paned bottom in round one, and capped on in square example; this edged up. Necks are tight, press-in fits, nicked and soldered inside. Lids peined down

bend on the wrong line—and it is not easy to bend back again. Make the "hooks" over the "hatchet" stakes or between the bending bars on the bench front (see sketch Fig 11E), knocking down fairly close over a thick steel rule or a bed lath—such as were used on the old iron bedsteads. The can body may then be conveniently bent or rounded by hand, passing it gradually over a half round bench bar or mandrel (and see that the double allowance hooks inwards) and working it so that no "corners" occur in the rounding process. It is fairly simple to round up bodywork to 12 in. diameter without bending rollers, and there is no reason why anyone should be unable to do so. An easily-made "folder" is shown at 11F. Having done that, place the body over the bench bar and, using the grooving punch, lightly secure the centre in two places, if the job is fairly long, say 12 in. or more, and once if shorter, then lightly secure the ends with the punch so that they cannot spring apart. Settle the job fairly upon the centre of the bar with the seam fair centre and proceed to complete the seamed joint, starting in the middle and working outwards each way. Do it fairly lightly first, so as not to unduly stretch the metal in any one locality, then finish up a bit harder, making sure the seam is properly fitted. Take care that the edges of the punch do not cut or crush the metal on each side of the seam ; if it does so it is likely to cause a crack. The mallet may be used now to flatten the rounded top of the seam ; use it from the centre outwards and you may follow up with a flat-faced planishing hammer judiciously applied just to make certain everything is closed up.

Finally, a little solder run along the inside of the seam will fix matters for good.

For an " inside " seam, same procedure takes place as regards the marking off.

The actual seaming of a large body may be done on the big surface-plate with the punch used inside the body, leaving a smooth outer contour. In Fig. 11I, for a small diameter job, use a grooved bar, and mallet the work into the groove. For short work I use the splined shafts from automobile gear boxes, these being of handy size for small jobs, beautifully true and hard, besides being easily obtained from the scrap piles. They will internally seam work down to 1½ in. diameter, and they may be gripped " short " in the vice.

In Fig. 12, the sketches show the various operations in throwing off an edge—a small flange in actual fact. This may be done on the jenny, but as this chapter relates to hand methods only, the way to work a jenny will be attended to later on. This edge may be done on a small anvil, on a piece of flat or square bar held in the vice, over the edge

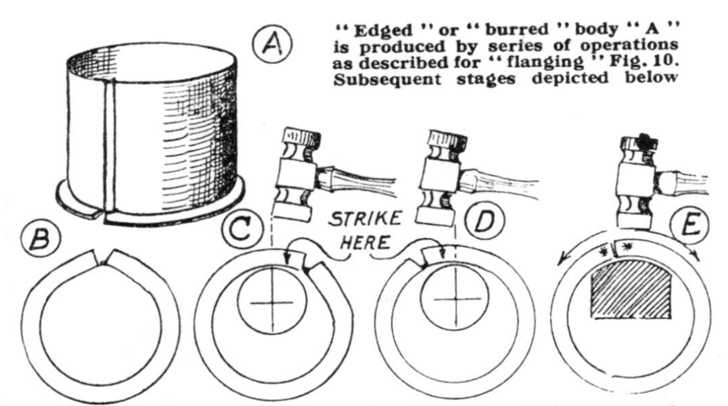

"Edged" or "burred" body "A" is produced by series of operations as described for "flanging" Fig. 10. Subsequent stages depicted below

Distorted body "B" often results through careless or hurried working. Place on a smallish bar with the "flat" part midway on bar and gently work into circularity as "C" and "D," doing first one side, then the other and finally truing up on a larger bar, working the job from side to side as in "E," keeping flange towards worker and striking behind it, there being less chance of damaging it so. Flange joint is neatly closed as "E" by lightly hammering the open tips * on anvil and dressing with a file

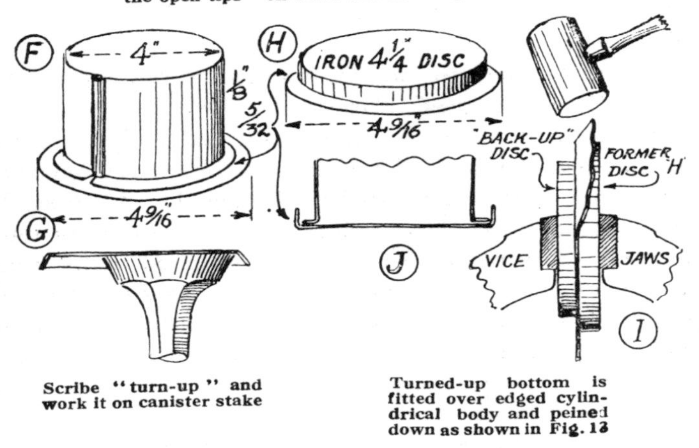

Scribe "turn-up" and work it on canister stake

Turned-up bottom is fitted over edged cylindrical body and peined down as shown in Fig. 13

Fig. 12.—Edging and seaming bottoms

of a surface plate or on a small creasing stake ; with care it may with equal facility be worked on the hatchet stake, as long as the sharpness of the edge is not too acute. Proceed as for "flanging" as in Chapter IV, Fig. 10, and carry on as Fig. 12, a, b, c. Upon the edge being nearly completed there will, doubtless, be a tendency for the job to go " out of round " ; there will be a " corner " where the seam comes. (See B). This must be carefully wangled out by hand pressure on the stake, using a small one inside and about $\frac{3}{4}$ in. each side of the seam. Work down with the hammer as C, D, until the irregularity is removed as near as possible. Then replace the work on the large stake or bench bar and carefully mallet, or still more carefully hammer, all over the work as Fig. 12E into a truly circular form. Judicious hammering will not unduly stretch the metal, nor will it mark it to any great extent. Here again, much depends upon the user, though there is really no reason why anyone with the desire to do so should not be able to handle a hammer so as to leave but barely perceptible marks.

The edge now having been successfully thrown off, it may be hammered flat either on the face or side of a suitable stake, or may be trued up as for " flanging," Fig. 10 D, E, F, after which the bottom plate or disc for the can may be proceeded with. For repetition jobs, and for jobs where such and such a size of bottom may often be needed at short notice, I keep a number of what I call " flanging plates," Fig. 12H and I, square, oval and round, in sizes that will do any such job as may crop up. These are variously made of cast iron, wrought iron, and hard wood. If a job done on one of these happens to work out just a wee bit too small for fitting over the can body, replace it on the plate and hammer it all over, starting in the centre and working out towards the edge, a procedure which will cause the metal to grow enough to fit over the work in hand. After this, go round the edge with a file and dress up any unevenly edged parts—this makes it look a bit better and only takes a minute.

Still another way to do it is shown in Fig. 12F and G. The edge is worked over a " Canister " stake, as shown in

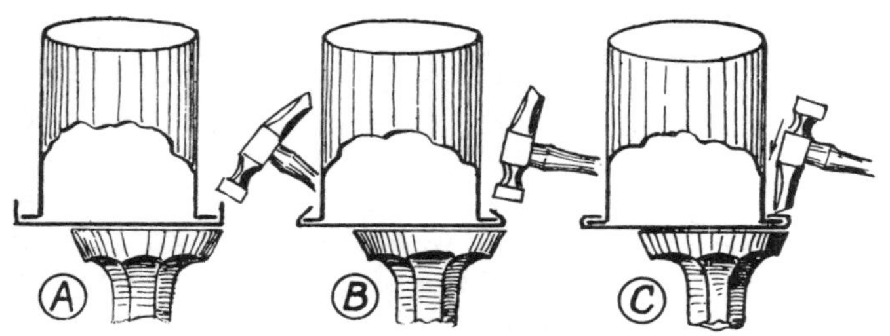

Work is stood on a "canister" or other flat stake at comfortable height as shown. Edge is "peined" down gradually, striking towards the inner edge to ensure neat joint but studiously avoiding hammer contact with the sides of the can or vessel.

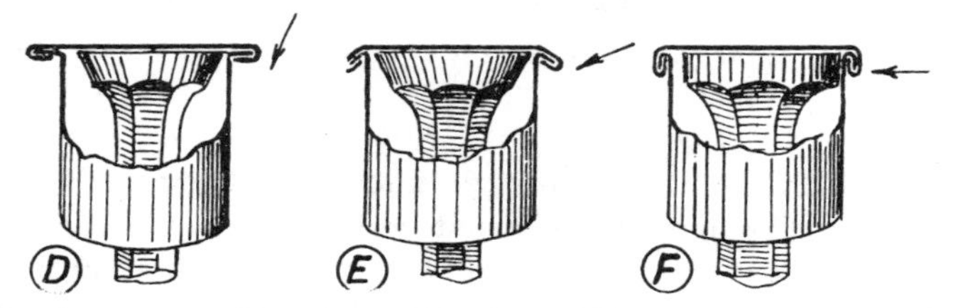

For the above "knocked-up" seams, canister stake is again used. Start with mallet. Flat-faced hammer for second and third stages, change the stake for a square edged one so that the seam can be hammered against it and not distort the sides.

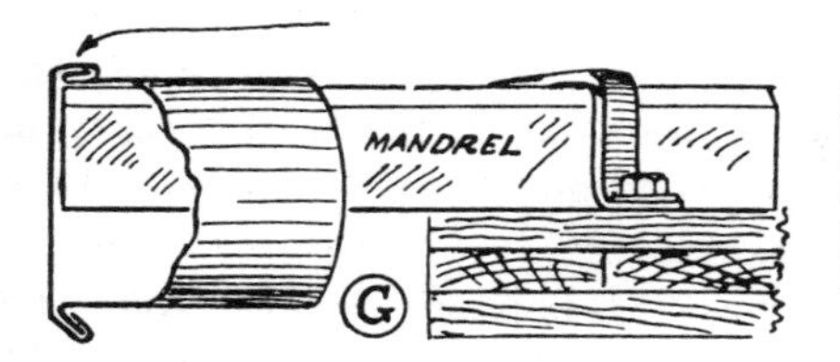

Canister stake may be held horizontally in the vice for more convenient working, or the job may be done on a suitable bench mandrel as shown. Large jobs must be so held

Fig. 13.—Peined-down and knocked-up seams and joints

Fig. 7E or a large gas engine valve—some are 3 in. or 4 in. in diameter with stems round about 1 in. diameter—which makes a very fine small stake for this and similar classes of work. A round piece of steel or iron welded to a round bar—or square for that matter—also does as good a job as a commercially-made metal working stake. Most of those I have used are improvisations of similar nature.

As mentioned in the beginning of the chapter, one easy way to arrive at a one-off bottom size is to lay the edged body centrally on the plate or disc, scribe round it and throw off an edge just clear of the line.

Lay the disc on the top of the stake, taking a look underneath to see that it is fair with the scribed circle at the point where a start is to be made, and knock down part way with the mallet as in 12G. Work the job round to another point a bit further and repeat until the job has gone a complete "round." Do it again and bring the edge over, say another 30 degrees all round, and for the third and final time finish off "square" and dress with the file.

The final fixing of the bottom to the can body is shown in Fig. 13A, B. C, in the style known as "peined-down" bottom. This is done on a flat stake again, or it may be done on a surface plate. Use a peining hammer, Fig. 3A or C, made so that the fore edge of the face hits the job tighter than the rear edge. Take care not to hit the can body near the bottom where the arrow points in C. It needs a bit of practice to avoid this but it can be avoided. Do it in three stages and try to draw the metal over so that there is but little space between the body and the inner edge of the finished joint. If you hit too hard an "edge-bound" bottom will result.

In this case what actually happens is that too much hammering at the outer edge causes this to grow and actually draw away from the rest of the metal forming the bottom. It cannot get away, as it is part of it, so it warps and refuses to lie flat. This trouble is to be touched upon later under the heading of "planishing," but a word or so here about this present difficulty may not be out of place. Place the can, bottom upwards, over a good, flat-faced, round stake and, beginning in the centre, gently and in successive rings, hammer towards the outer edge until the can will lie flat on the surface plate. Do not do

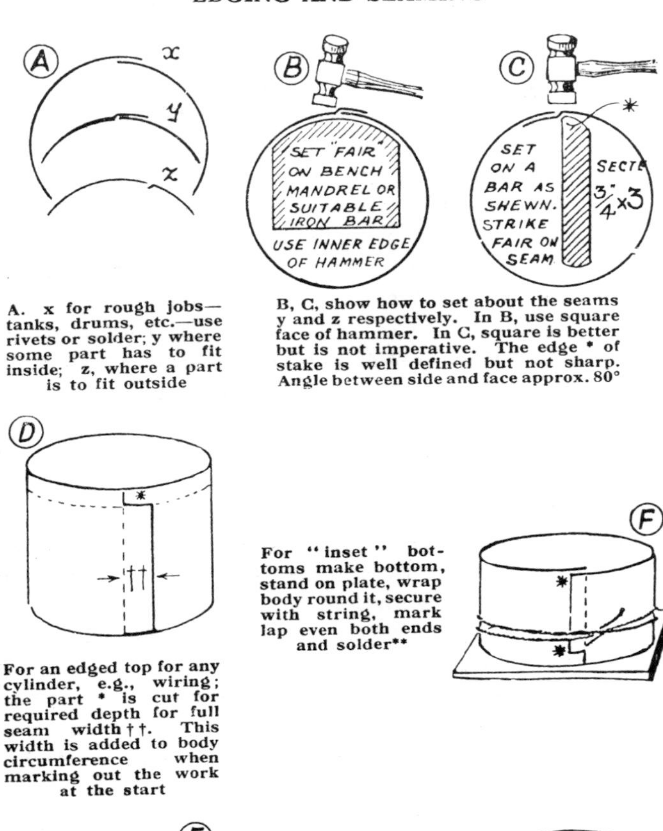

A. x for rough jobs—tanks, drums, etc.—use rivets or solder; y where some part has to fit inside; z, where a part is to fit outside

B, C, show how to set about the seams y and z respectively. In B, use square face of hammer. In C, square is better but is not imperative. The edge * of stake is well defined but not sharp. Angle between side and face approx. 80°

For an edged top for any cylinder, e.g., wiring; the part * is cut for required depth for full seam width † †. This width is added to body circumference when marking out the work at the start

For "inset" bottoms make bottom, stand on plate, wrap body round it, secure with string, mark lap even both ends and solder**

E

"Capped-on" bottom

1

Anti-wear inset

2

Ordinary flat in-set bottoms, usually in cheap cans, drums, etc.

In case E it is usual to make the body to size, measure and cut bottom with edging allowance and work up on canister stake, former, or with jenny

Fig. 14.—Plain lapped seams, and capped-on and inset bottoms

too much with the hammer, or the bottom will be like an oil can—go in and out and spin on its centre when it is "out." Go easy all the time, and try it now and then to see that it does not get "loose" in the middle.

Having got so far with the *peined-down* seam style, you may wish to proceed to the *knocked-up* seam, as shown in Fig. 13, D to G. For this, do not attempt to get such a close and neat-fitting bottom in the earlier stages as when proceeding with stages E, F; there is considerable "draw" taking place. The inner edge of the peined bottom in this case should be clear of the body by a full sheet metal thickness as it has to accommodate such an amount tucked up inside as in F. In *knocking up* all the strain is a "draw" away from the centre—all the bottom is in tension.

The plain lapped seams and "capped-on" and inset bottoms featured in Fig. 14 require practically no explanation. For the seam, all that is needed is the one lap. Measure the exact circumference of the body, add the desired lap and that is that. So far as the type of seam, either outside or inside-flush is concerned, Fig. 14 B and C show the method.

The method of edging has been shown in Fig. 12, using the "former-plate"; fixing the bottoms is plain work.

With a "capped-on" bottom, the body is soldered first and the bottom "capped-on" and soldered.

With the inset style, the body may be fitted round the bottom, or the body may be soldered up or riveted and the bottom made to fit inside. For this, allow a couple of metal-thicknesses on the "small side," in fact it pays to err on the small side anyway. You can always stretch the flange a bit so that it will fit the body tighter. I prefer to make bottoms first, tying the bodies to fit, soldering or tacking in place and then soldering all together. Take care, though, that the whole "issue" does not come adrift during the process; and that you do not lose your scribed lap marks.

CHAPTER VI

WIRING EDGES BY HAND

NEARLY everything in the sheet metal way is wired somewhere or other. It may be asked why such should be the case ; the answer is that this is about the easiest way to enhance appearance, and add strength at the same time. The one operation serves for both.

The initial procedure is much the same for this as for ordinarily throwing off an edge or small flange. Allowance for wire is as previously stated, bare 4 wire diameters. Allow this below the top edge and cut as in Fig. 11D.

At about two-thirds of the way down from the top throw off to an angle similarly to starting a flange (see Fig. 10A), taking care that the actual " bend " is not deeply marked by the edge of stake. Do this with the mallet, to be sure. Then, at about the half depth of the wiring allowance, begin to throw off a second bend and carry this to about right angles to the cylindrical or hemispherical body (as this operation holds good for a bowl as well). Knock this back all round over a piece of bent iron or steel held in the vice as shown in Fig. 15G and F (section). Again, for repetition jobs, I use a number of such " stakes " made to various curvatures. When the turned-down edge is nearly a true U, insert the wire, run it right round the job, see that it is tucked in under the cut away seam and mark where the loose end comes against the parent wire in the coil, which may conveniently be on the floor. Cut at this mark, and then take the wire out and file the edges so that there are no sharp corners to cut through the metal when finally hammering up the wired edge. The two ends may be safely left about 1/16 in. apart when initially tried in position, as in closing in the turn-over everything tends to tighten up.

Having reinserted the wire, place the job over a bench mandrel or a half-round bench stake and knock over the edge of the turn-up so that it nearly covers the wire. Do this in about three stages, using a drawing motion of the mallet towards yourself—the actual hammer or mallet head describes an arc towards the user as at J, Fig. 15. In Figs. 5A and 15I are shown pairs of pliers. These were an ordinary pair of long-nose flat pliers, of the non-wire cutting type—just flat-nosed pliers. With a good quality hacksaw and slow motion, cut $\frac{3}{4}$ in. off the jaws and grind or file the inside part of what is left so that the shape is as shown. When "closed," the jaws are actually open about a full $\frac{1}{8}$ in. at the outer ends and taper backwards to about 3/16 in. inside. It may be said that a few pairs of such pliers will be very useful for finally drawing over a wired edge. I do not use a wiring machine and do all wiring aided by these pliers; and by hand have wired stuff using $\frac{1}{4}$ in. wire. The pliers used for this were a pair of 8 in. converted glaziers' type, and they performed handsomely. After this procedure, the wired edge may be trued up again over the bench stakes and then placed on the "creasing iron" or stakes, with the wired edge fitting into an appropriate groove and malleted down all round with a curved-faced mallet, as in Fig. 15H. This procedure holds good also for wiring in the straight; in fact all the foregoing may be applied to straight wiring, except, of course, the rounding operations. The U formation may be made over a special thin, but rounded, edge hatchet stake. A modified type can be made up by screwing or welding a piece of $\frac{1}{8}$ in. or 3/16 in. steel strip to an iron bar to grip in the vice as shown in Fig. 15K.

On some occasions it has been necessary to wire ornamental metal trays, and the procedure then was to block

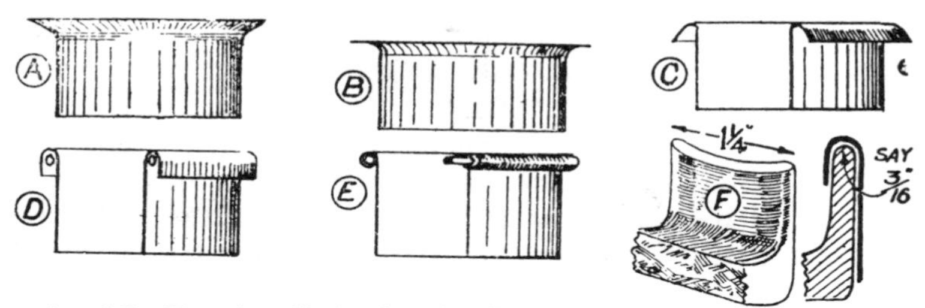

A and B.—Throwing-off edge for wire. Procedure as Figs. 10 and 12
C and D.—Edge turned back. Use stake F

F.—Wiring stake—Ends rounded on edge and 3 or 4 in. radii for one stake. Other pairs may be made to suit jobs

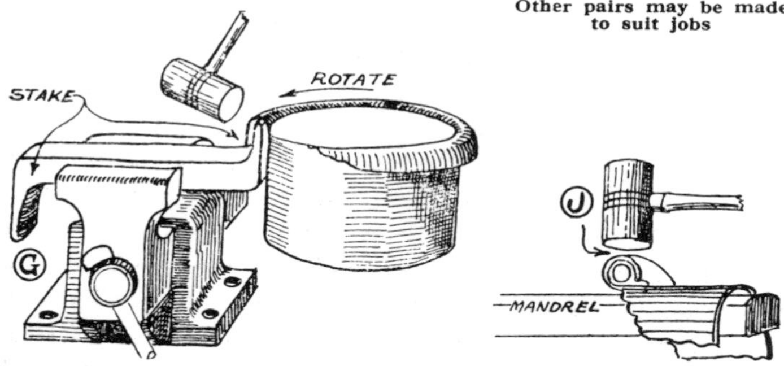

G.—Stake held in vice and used for forming turn-up for wire. Hollow face is outward

J.—Section on wired rim. Closing wired edge with mallet over bench bar or mandrel

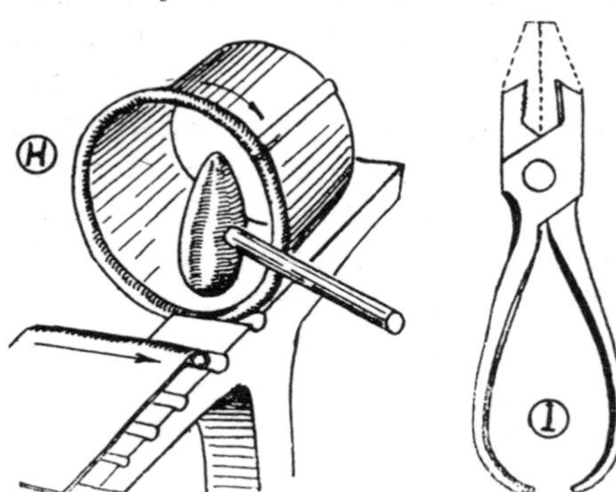

K.—Vice "stake" for wire edging of flat work. Use as in G

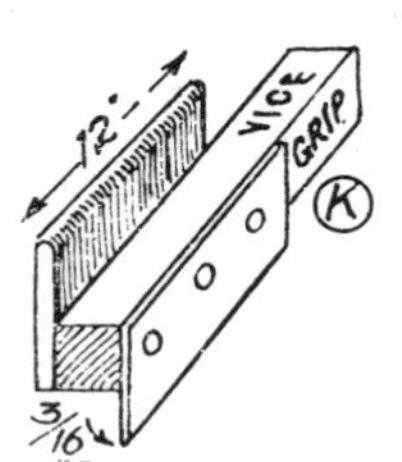

H.—Closing or setting in a wire. Round or flat work done on crease

I.—"Faked" closing pliers. Jaws ground or filed (according to quality) as above

Fig. 15.—Wiring cylindrical work

out the tray to the desired depth and diameter, throw off an edge as previously explained, and then finish off the U turnover. A ring of suitable diameter was formed of $1\frac{1}{2}$ in. × $\frac{1}{8}$ in. bar iron and butt welded. The tray was placed into this and the edge knocked over all round and snugly against the sides of the iron ring. The result was that the job retained its circularity, the turn over was uniform, and the operation performed in satisfactory time.

Mention must be made of the location of the wire join with reference to the seamed joint of a cylindrical job. My practice is to keep this wire join as far away as practicable—preferably opposite the seam in work that is wired subsequently to rounding up.

CHAPTER VII

JENNIES AND WIRING MACHINES

A CONSIDERABLE amount of sheet-metal work may be done without either of these tools. As they are comparatively expensive, the small worker may not feel justified in purchasing them, and the methods described for hand working will enable him to do most, if not all the work coming to him. For many years I did without and got them in the end only because they had the reputation for being "quicker."

Even now, if there is a number of small bottoms or canister bodies or the like to edge or wire, former-plates and flanging plates, aided by the faked pliers for wiring, leave me with little to be desired for speed of operation. For everyday or small stuff those jennies are rarely used and, with some shame be it said, are rusting away contentedly below the bench. They are about the only bits of gear that are rusty because everything else is more or less regularly used. The old blacksmith who tacked up in his shop a notice:—"No rest—No rust! No trust—No bust!" knew what was what.

If you fancy your work demands the possession of these tools, get them. If in doubt, but anxious to spend money, spend it on more hand kit—stakes, mandrels, shears, and so on, but do not buy and allow to rust.

Why both should not be called "jennies" is difficult to fathom, for they perform practically the same sort of work. The jenny edges work with a sharp corner, such as can bottoms, etc., and the wiring machine edges work very similarly, but with a rounded turn-up for the reception of a wire. Having performed this operation, substitution of the top roller or wheel for a different type will enable the user to " tuck-in " his metal over the wire. The sketches show the similarity between the two machines, and explains why, until familiar with them, you may be excused for mixing them up. Both look like " jennies," and it would need fairly sensitive fingers to select one from the other in a bad light.

Sizes vary though, sometimes, as also do small details. Actually, when on a job that requires both edging and wiring, I do three operations on the one tool—the jenny proper.

One may certainly prepare a wiring edge on a disc with a jenny—it is done in stages—as will be shown later on. The " tucking-in " part of the job also will be explained. In fact, many tricks can be done with these machines, just as one learns how to juggle with hand tools.

The sketches show both machines and the " key " applies to both of them from a working and constructional point of view. Any slight difference will be explained subsequently.

In Fig. 16, A and B, the main body casting is shown at (9). This has a tapered tang to fit into a bench or bench block—it may even be held in the vice. Hinged to the upper portion of the body is the main spindle arm or bracket (5) in which runs the spindle (6) integral with which is the edging roller (2) which works in the stepped groove in the bottom roller or forming roller (3). The fence or gauge (1) is adjustable for width of metal to be turned up, and is adjusted laterally by the wingnut or thumbscrew (8). The location of this adjustment may vary with various makes, but the fence or gauge is invariably in that position.

The desired turn-up having been decided upon for a batch of work—a procedure which calls for some practice and judgment—the gauge is set so that the required amount of disc edge protrudes under the top roller. This roller is screwed down now, by means of screw-handle (4), until, with the disc about horizontal, the action of the rollers will just nicely rotate it. Note that as you turn the handle *towards* you the work rotates *away* from you.

Hold it at its outer edge, fingers underneath, and let it

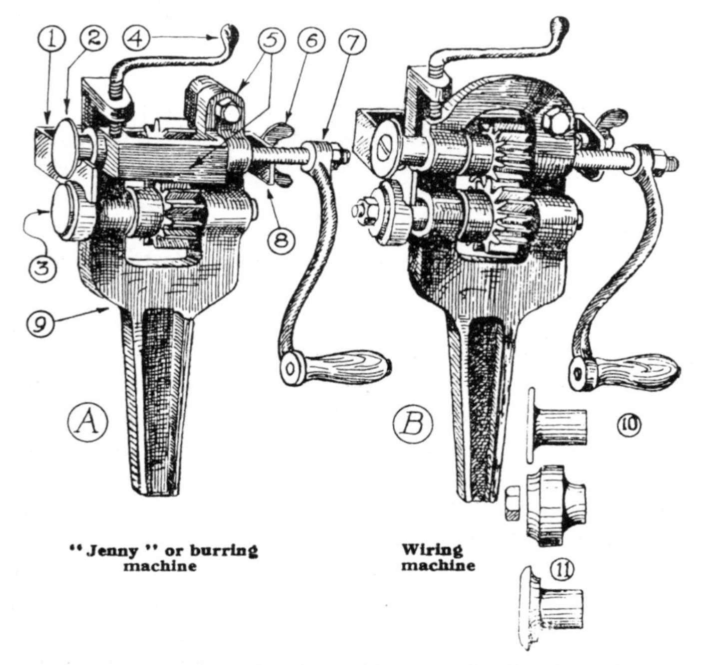

(1) Fence or gauge. (2) "Turn-up" roller. (3) Forming roller. (4) Pressure screw. (5) Hinged spindle arm. (6) Main spindle. (7) Handle. (8) Screw for adj. gauge (No. 1). (9) Main body casting and tang for bench. (10) These rollers (usually four pairs) are for various wire thicknesses and turn the edge for reception of wire. Top one fixed with "flush" screw. (11) "Tuck-in" rollers used singly (two provided) fit top spindle and close the metal over the wire, the bottom roller meanwhile acting as a "holder-up"

Fig. 16.—Jennies and wiring machines

just trail through the grip. Do not try forcing it and do not unconsciously "grip" it hard enough to hold it back. The action is quite simple, and a very light pressure on the screw will enable one to edge a bottom at one setting. Ordinarily, though, the tyro feels compelled to screw down a wee turn, so as to get the rolls to " grip " after the first revolution or so. The job comes out of the rollers and very often leaves nasty marks where the top roller " gripped " or failed to do so—to the beginner's surprise. I can scarcely describe or explain how to keep the work there, otherwise than to advise a light pressure towards the rolls and a more or less lightly persuasive tilt upwards with the guiding hand while the work rotates. If you try very hard to keep the job there, the chances are that it will not stay there at all. Screwing hard on the screw handle will make the job stick or else badly crinkle. Again, it may be said, the best speed is obtained by going slowly and letting the job more or less " do itself." That is for just ordinary bottom edging or burring. However, one little tip must not be overlooked. After cutting out a disc or batch of discs, run the back of the snips all round the cut edges back and front to burnish off the razor-like edge left thereon. Failing this, a very nasty cut may be had at the root of the left thumb as the work slides through between thumb and fingers.

A glance at Fig. 17 A and B will help you to understand these explanations of working.

Not only will a jenny edge up a disc, but it will do all sorts of things to cylindrical work. Fig. 17C is an example. You set your fence (1) or guide to the scribed line, nip down a wee bit on the hand-screw (4) and turn the job round, the driving handle going anti-clockwise. Gradually altering the angle of the work, its axis will presently assume the position of the disc shown above at B—very nearly vertical. By this time the edge will have been satisfactorily " thrown off " so that you will have what you see at the other end. Anyhow, that is your object. The main idea is to avoid nipping down too hard on the hand-screw. Now a step further. We will suppose you have edged your end nicely and that you want to join it up endways

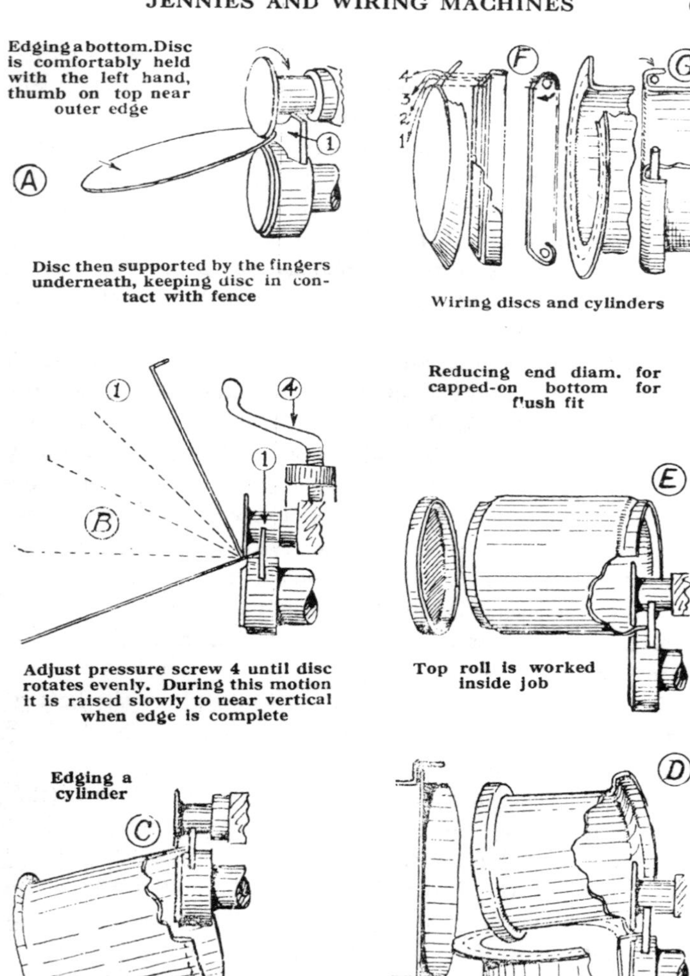

Fig. 17.—Using jenny on flat and cylindrical work

with another piece of work—say a kitchen steam-pan—a double bodied affair that you have seen and may own. To join a pair of such cylindrical bodies, edge the first, say $\frac{1}{8}$ in., and for the second one, scribe a 9/32 in. edge. Having done this, place the first against the second, see how much margin there is, set the fence to that amount bare and follow Fig. 17D. Start with the cylinder vertical and finish with it nearly horizontal, and the top sketch should give you an idea of the result you should get. Offer the two together, trim just a bit here and there off the first one until it fits, and then hold the seam against a side stake, pan stake, bick or crease, and pein down the edge as in Fig. 13, A, B, C, though in this case you will not be able to stand it on the stake to work it up; you will only be able to rest the seam on the edge of whichever stake you use. You may have to fix a division plate or disc between the two bodies for some reason or other—maybe an automobile silencer or an invention for a client. If you do, cut it the same size as the first edged cylinder and place it in the other one and do the whole job just as if the division plate were not there.

Now imagine that you have a job to do where the bottom has to be right flush with the body; and it has to be a capped-on bottom.

For this, the fence (Fig. 17E) is set just a bit farther away from the top roll than the depth of the edged bottom, and the top roll is worked inside the can body, exactly the reverse of C. Proceed with the job until the lid or bottom, whichever it is, will just fit snugly on. It may be necessary to remove the work once or twice just to see what the "fit" is like, but it is no trouble whatever to replace and pick up the old setting of the top roll. Should it inadvertently be made too small, all that needs to be done is to place the work over a mandrel and lightly tap the adjacent part of the body. This will bring pressure against the reduced part and slightly open it out. Do not overdo this or the jenny will be needed again. A little care in manipulation solves the problem.

The top right-hand group (Fig. 17, F and G) shows the processes involved in using the jenny for wiring. For a 3/32 in. wire, set the jenny gauge about 5/16 in. inwards, and partly throw off a 5/16 in. edge to about the angle shown. (See F, 1, 2, 3 and 4.) Re-set about 3/32 in. closer to the roll and take another turn round the work ; in another 1/32 in. and yet again a bit tighter, and the result will be like the second stage shown. Lay the work on a flat surface plate or anvil-stake and mallet over as in the third sketch, insert wire, cut to length so that the ends will not exactly butt, and mallet right over. Next set the fence so that the top roll just bites the newly-turned edge, and starting with the work somewhere near the final stage shown in B—nearly vertical—run the disc round a few times and the top roll will tuck in the edge. It may be said that although easy to do, this last operation takes a little practice before really good results are obtained.

Continuing jenny-wiring, the sketches G show two stages in wiring a cylindrical body. Throw off a 5/16 in. to $\frac{3}{8}$ in. edge. Reduce the setting about $\frac{1}{8}$ in. and do the turn over. This may be done in three settings similar to F ; that is, three settings subsequent to the initial " throw off." Insert the wire, cut to length, mallet over either on a stake or mandrel, close with the top roll as for F—and that is all.

In Fig. 18H is a case where an edged bottom is too slack a fit for a body. Such a body may be too thick to hammer out to a greater diameter, or for some other reason it may be imperative that the end be reduced. This is done in exactly the same way as the can body in Fig. 17E. Compare the two operations.

Suppose a strainer disc or other wired plate was what is called " loose " in the middle, and it was desired to stiffen it without planishing it. Being wired, it is nearly impossible to " planish " it because such curative treatment would have to be round the edges for a " sloppy " centre, and hammering such a wired job would not do it much good; it might even buckle the wired edge. Turn the wired disc " wire-down " (Fig. 18I), set the top jenny roll just clear of the wired edge, put a very little pressure on the hand-screw and carry on with the wheeling motion until the disc rises to about the angle shown. The result is that the top roll has drawn the metal away from the centre and formed a " bead " opposite the wired edge. This process may be carried to such a degree that the original wired edge is " flush " and the entire beading thrown up on the " good " side. Such a procedure is often made use of in the production of, say, a wall plaque, a metal dish stand, a flat teapot stand, and so on.

The last example, Fig. 18J, is the same operation performed on straight work. Can handles or bows are done this way.

Some of the heavier classes may be wired first and then wheeled over. Insert on your own side, turn the handle towards you and the work comes " out back." Take two or three passes if necessary until the requisite depth of bead is obtained and you can run right through a batch at one pass. Sketches a, b show sections of ordinary edged and beaded work; c, d are examples of wired and beaded. Besides adding a degree of finish, this process certainly enhances the stiffness of such work. The little extra trouble is certainly not wasted. One can run round the edges of a big rectangular wired draining board in the same way. It is a bit unwieldly, but it can be done.

Wiring Machines

Fig. 16B illustrates a wiring machine. Sketched, as it intentionally is, alongside a jenny, it brings out those points of similarity already mentioned.

The components " key " is identical except for sketches 10, 11, which replace the integral rolls in the case of the jenny.

The top wiring roll is secured on a squared end on the main spindle by a flush countersunk screw, or in some cases, a flush cap-nut. This is because discs and other work have to assume a more or less vertical position in final wiring stages similar to that of parts being worked on the jenny, as in Fig. 17B. A nut and screwed end would be an obstruction. The lower roll does not matter, and is fixed with a nut as usual.

These top and bottom rolls, as shown in Fig. 16, are usually supplied in sets of four pairs on new machines, the top thin roll being of similar thickness to the diameter or gauge of wire to be used. The lower one has a half-groove to correspond, except that this groove has to be a

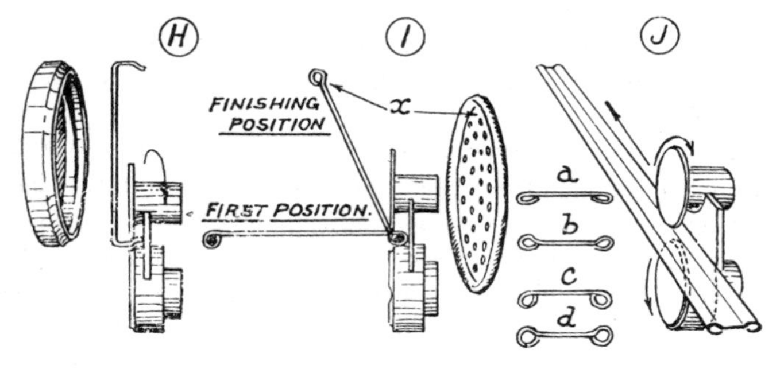

Reducing a cap-on bottom. Fence is set so that top roll is 1/16 in. inside the edge, action being to reduce edge diam. to desired "fit" on a can or other body

Beading edge on wired disc. Fence is set so that top roller clears wired edge. With disc "wire down," beaded edge is made with top roll, which forces down inner surface x

Beading edged on wired strip. Operation performed as one previous but strip passed under roll in one direction only as shown once or twice; a.c. edged and wired ,b.d. beaded only

Fig. 18.—Further examples of jenny work

shade larger radius to allow for the thickness of the sheet to be worked thereon.

The "tuck-in" roll is interchangeable with the top roll and is used for turning the edge of sheet right down the wire. It is worked very similarly to the jenny when used for that purpose, as earlier described in Fig. 17, F, G, but it does the job properly as it is designed for the purpose. It does not need a lot of "wangling," nor does it necessitate the disc or other work being canted to such a high angle. Moreover, it cannot slip during the process as can the jenny. However, failing possession of such a machine, quite a good job may be done with its partner, or even by hand.

CHAPTER VIII

BEADING AND SWAGING MACHINES

THESE tools are constructed so much on the lines of jennies and wiring machines that a detailed description is unnecessary.

The interchangeable rollers have a variety of grooves and series of grooves round each, the contours of which are male and female. One sees the work done by such tools round the ends of bins, heavy milk cans, oil drums, cooling tanks and fuel tanks, in fact any container of nearly any shape, where such treatment is beneficial either to strengthen the formation or enhance appearance—very often both. Various patterns of such rolls are shown in Fig. 19, They are used in pretty much the same way as the jennies ; the fence or guide is set at a suitable distance so that the swaging or beading rollers produce the formation at the correct distance from the end of the receptacle, or whatever the work may be. Adjustment is similar, in many cases identical ; the handle operation is towards the user also.

On type is especially made with a very deep "throat," and has a long reach so that a cylinder may be swaged or beaded round its mid-section.

No explanation is needed for cylindrical work, but in swaging a rectangular piece the object is inserted, suitably screwed down to correct rolling adjustment, and traversed away from the operator until the rolls bring up against the adjacent side, Ease off and bring back until the rollers touch the other side ; now screw down again and go a bit deeper, repeating the operation. By this time the swage track will have become sufficiently well defined to keep correct line. All subsequent rollings of this article may be done with a full movement back and forth, just " screwing down " a bit each time until the swaged grooves are a desired depth. It will be obvious, however, that these grooves must stop about half-roller-diameter from each corner in any rectangular job. Also, in the case of a heavily made grooved seamed job, one cannot expect the rollers to jump a ridge of four metal thicknesses. Just stop short at the seam each time and go on again.

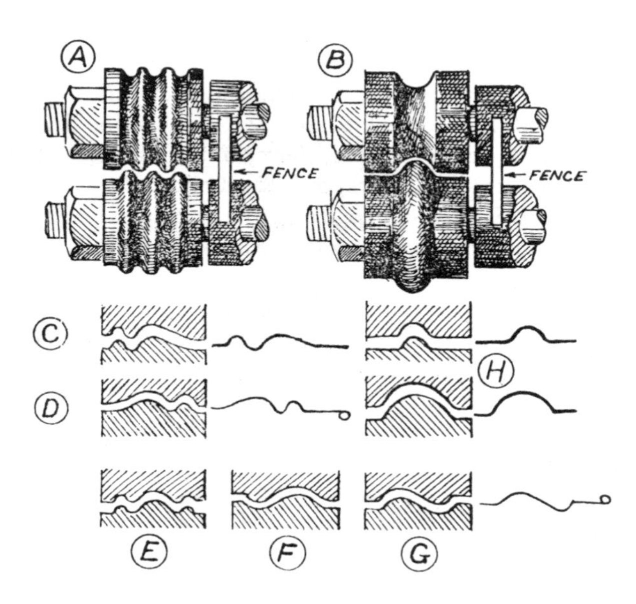

Rolls A and E are ornamental swages very often used midway on a cylindrical job. Those shown at C and F may be used for strengthening or for ornament. Type D (reverse of C) is often used adjacent to an internally wired rim so that a mating part may fit down over it and butt against the smaller swaged rim. G is similar to D and is used adjacent to a rim wired externally to accommodate an inner fitting. In cases D and G the fence is set for required depth of rim and wired edge worked against it. B are plain beading rolls, used mainly for ends of cylinders where they fit into a top component or a base

Fig. 19.—Swaging and beading machines

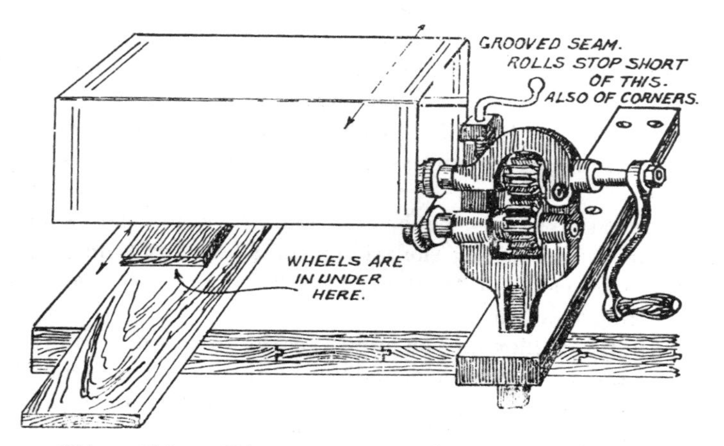

36 in. × 24 in. × 10 in. × 18 s.w.g. tank mounted on rollers (from roller skate) at level of beading rolls. Positive roll is worked below so as to press the bead up into tank, and to keep the edge being worked at constant level without packings

Fig. 20.—A "roller" idea for beading

Inside Beads

A single inside bead is very useful for locating against a tank end and makes a really solid job. (See Beading Rolls, Fig. 19B.) Such a job is referred to in the later constructional notes.

Outside Beads

An outer swaged or beaded cylinder is often worked where such has to fit into a foundation ring. This keeps it from falling through, and keeps it "straight" whilst sweating, etc.

While on the subject of work done on these tools, Fig. 20 may be of interest. Actually it was recalled to mind during the drawing and writing of a later chapter, but it is considered more suitable for inclusion in this present one on working beaders, etc.

Fig. 20 is nearly enough self-explanatory, so that little need be said regarding the idea or the working.

It looks rather a comical rig-up, but in such small shops as mine one has to fake many gadgets and make-shifts that would make a real production foreman throw up his hands—possibly his job too—if he was expected to work with such meagre kit and very often at literally a moment's notice.

Round tanks may be beaded and/or swaged the same way, or at least using the trolley, or whatever it may be, only in this case you want the tank to rotate in the beader or swaging machine.

Turn the trolley upside down, pack up to the required height and let the tank or cylindrical body just roll round on the upturned gadget. It will pretty nearly work and guide itself.

CHAPTER IX

CONICAL WORK

Pattern Development

BEFORE one can construct a cone a pattern must be made or else drawn directly upon the metal to be cut.

Conical patterns are, perhaps, the easiest of all of those used in sheet metal work and also, from my experience, the most universally required. Very few objects but have a cone somewhere in their general make up, some may be very slight, others more marked, but cones will be found to be very common. There are buckets, oil can " top " portions, watering cans, funnels for liquids, bench oil cans, light shades, stove pipe caps, measures—the list is unending.

There are various methods of arriving at such a pattern : some are on more or less academic lines, with plenty of figure work to do, others again are a matter of elementary geometry—just a few arcs and lines together with the bare elevational dimensions of the proposed cone.

It is unlikely that any very large cones will be cut and made up in the ordinary small establishment, so instructions will be confined to such as can be struck with a pair of long-leg compasses, a pair of trammels or strip of wood or metal and two nails—even string at a pinch.

In Fig. 21, sketch A, the required cone is shown in elevation a, b, c, d. Construction throughout is as follows : a, b, is the base, make it to suit the cone. With compasses set to ab or *any* dimension near that, strike the arcs **x** first from a, then from b, and another pair z bisecting the base. Through the intersection of these arcs draw the centre line op truly perpendicular to base line and of indefinite length. Anywhere on or outside ab, with radius op, describe two more arcs rs. Exactly tangent to rs draw a line as shown. Set compasses to half top cone diameter and with that radius describe from p two more arcs intersecting rps at cd. This cd is the diameter of the desired conical form, and a b c d is the elevation as mentioned above. All that has been needed or will be needed is a rule and a pair of compasses for most ordinary dimensions.

The required pattern is obtained as follows: Produce the sides a c and b d to intersect at y, from which point the compasses, trammels or stick and nails are set to radius ya or yb and the arc g a b h described. From this point y, again, with the lesser radius yc or yd, describe the top arc ecdf to indefinite length. Setting the compasses at ab dimension, from a and b respectively describe the arcs intersecting the base-line arc at g and h.

Join gy and hy and the *nett conical pattern* is that enclosed within the letters efgh. If for a plain " lap " seam, allow one lap width only. If for a " grooved " seam allow three widths of " hook " as in Chapter V, Fig. 11.

These must be drawn *parallel to the pattern ends*—not converging towards centre.

Allow, also, on the nett pattern, a full three metal thicknesses for the bends in the " hook " seams. The patterns, as drawn, being on paper have no thickness. In large work, using the average 24 to 20 s.w.g. material, bending losses are not so noticeable, but when working up small patterns, unless such allowances for bending losses are included, the finished diameters will be 1/16 in. or more " small." For most ordinary work this will not matter much, but if such forms are intended to *fit* into a definite and pre-determined size of edged bottom or lid, they will be too small, and the cone will have to be stretched by hammering all round to expand to fit. This is no great trouble, but means waste of time.

It may have been supposed that the easiest way to draw

such a pattern is arrived at by striking a large arc 3 1/7 times the dimension ab, *i.e.*, circumference 3 1/7 times diameter. It is not so easy to measure 1/7 of any such dimensions that may crop up, though again, there is a graphical way of doing that with a rule and a set-square (or even a postcard at a pinch). Anyway, it is a job to step a seventh of a

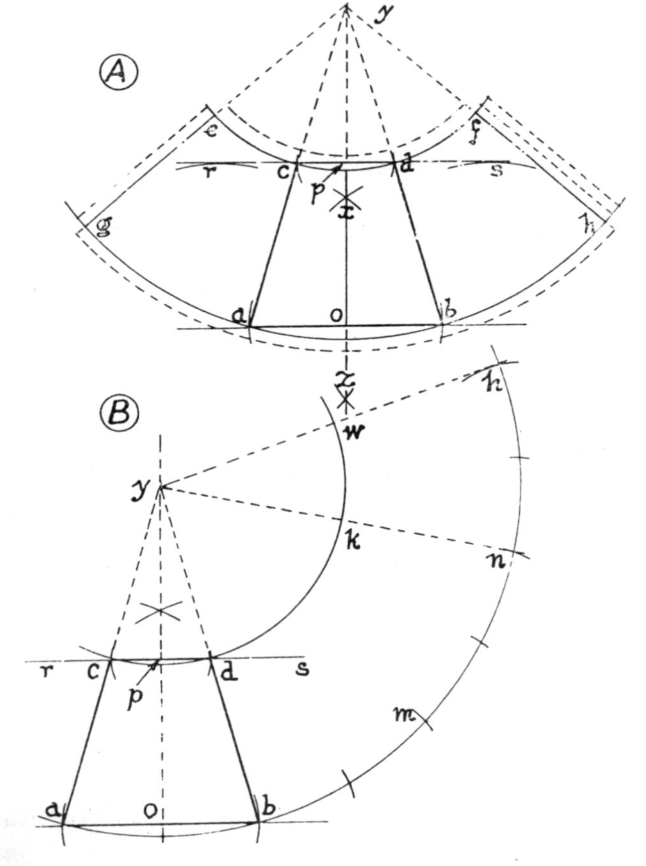

Fig. 21.—Patterns for conical work. Graphical methods

straight line accurately, a number of times round a curved one and as the probable errors are accumulative, results are not to be depended upon, and it is not proposed to deal with this particular method.

Fig. 21B shows an alternative method of arriving at a similar result.

As before, construct the elevation of the truncated cone a b c d. With radius ya or yb, describe major arc through ab and then step off arc ab at bm, mn. Join yn. Describe arc ck with radius yc or yd and the pattern represented within ankc is identical with the one above and includes the "elevation." Should material not be at hand to make up a complete pattern, this trouble may be got over by doing the job " in twice."

Draw a half-elevation only, pobd and step ob along twice to m, which is three ob dimensions inclusive. Cut two off in paper. Gum together on a backing strip with ends butting or make on half pattern with a lap joint to gum under the other half pattern.

Pattern dwhb excludes the " elevation." Remember that allowances for seaming and for the " hook " seam bending losses must only be added to the completed whole pattern.

Top and bottom flanging, edging or wiring allowances are, of course, more easily added during the constructional stages of the pattern drawing when the main centre point y is present—before any cutting takes place.

Any type of cone, " blunt or sharp," may be done this way. It may mean that a piece of brown paper or big piece of cardboard will have to be drawing-pinned to the floor, and long radii contrived by a wooden staff with a bradawl at one end and a pencil through a friction-tight hole at the other. Inches, etc., pencilled on the staff, the awl pushed through at the correct increments of measurement and used as pivot. Used with ordinary care, no important discrepancies in measurements have been noticed. Big work will

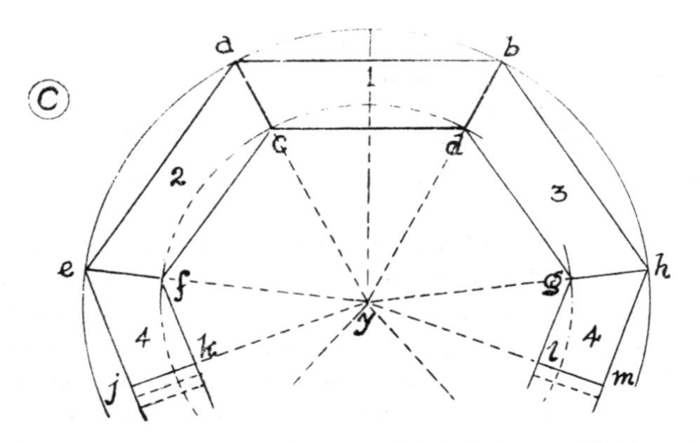

a, b, c, d is an elevation of a square-conical or pyramidal form. Pattern shown is suitable for small work and may be cut out in one piece

Template for work of slow taper

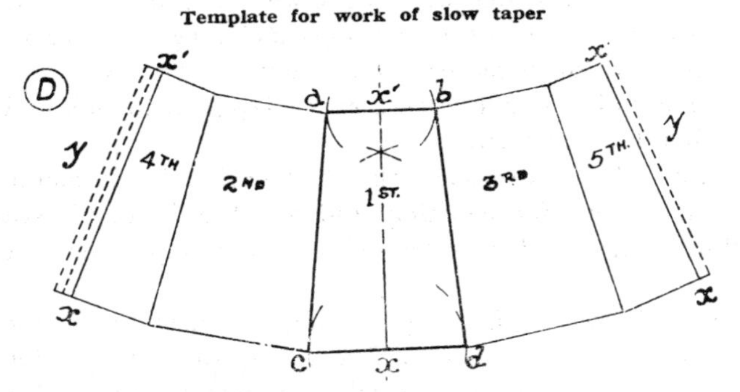

Elevation a, b, c, d is first drawn complete with centre-line on thin cardboard and cut out, laid on to another piece, it is copied off three times and then two halves. Add seaming or wiring allowances y-y.

Fig. 22.—Pyramidal or square cones

stand a little error here and there. With small work the closer one measures the better the results. An extra 3/32 in. on a small circumference and a bottom will not even " spring on."

Before passing on to working methods there are one or two other points which may be touched upon with regard to what may be termed "true cones," or cones which do actually run to a point neither truncated nor open-topped.

In the case of a cone where the slant width (some call it "height," by the way) cone-side or hypotenuse is equal to the base or diameter, the required pattern is a semi-circle. To this semi-circle, of course, there must be added the necessary lap or groove-seam allowances, unless for a butt-joint which will be reinforced or plated-up inside, in which case

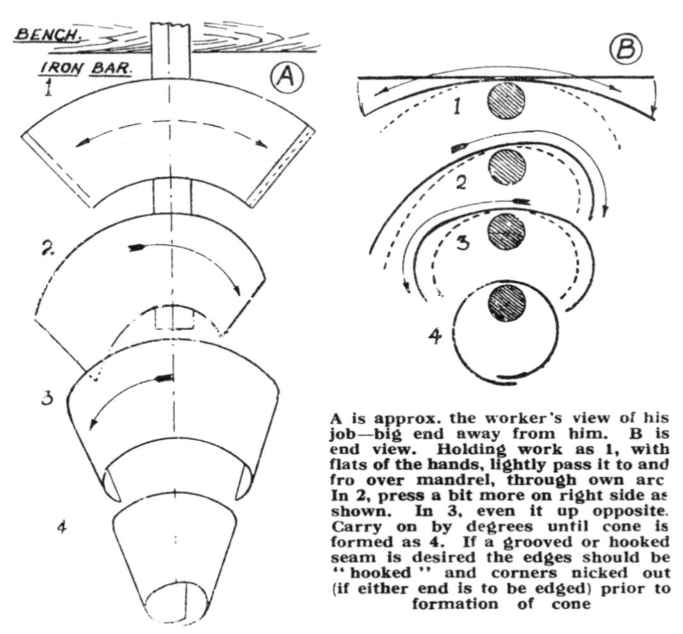

Fig. 23.—Working a cone by hand

the nett pattern is used. Further, so as to work such a cone easily on the funnel stake, bick iron or anvil, it is best to file a small semi-circle out of the centre part. One cannot bend a cone round a dot or rather a half of a dot, but a small semi-circular recess, say 3/16 diameter, will work round to a true point with care.

Where the base is half the hypotenuse or slant width or cone side, we get something like the old candle-extinguisher and this may be made up from a quarter of a circle. The extreme point must be cut off to work this. Add the lap allowance.

Where the base is one-and-a-half times the cone side the

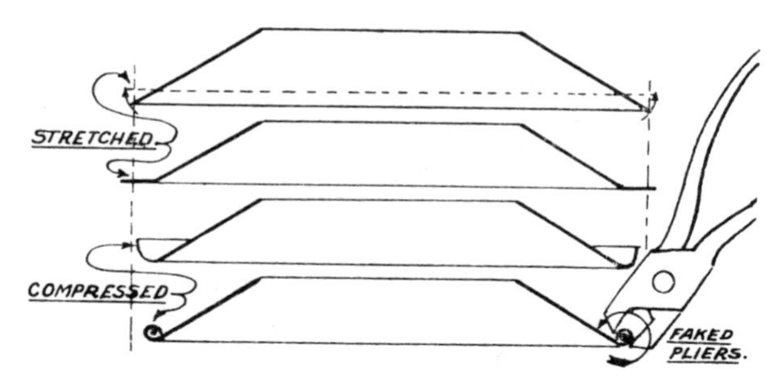

Fig. 23a.—Effect of wiring a cone

pattern developed is three-quarters of a circle. Add lap and observe precautions for working the point.

" Square " Conical, or Pyramidal Forms

These forms are also cut from patterns or templates which are produced graphically. In certain types of ornamental work they may be made from four side-plates riveted together on to gussets or corner plates. In the case of one type of domestic utensil—the baking pan or dish—the templates may be worked from one piece—a rather interesting procedure.

A sketch of the graphical pattern method is shown in Fig. 22 CD.

In the top sketch abcd is the elevation of say, a baking dish. The easiest way to do this pattern is first to cut out the bare elevation. Lay this on a big sheet of brown paper, go round it with a fine pencil, then lay it against each of sides ac and bd in turn and pencil it on to the paper. Add half the elevation to each of 2 and 3, (*i.e.* 4 and 4 in the sketch), and add your seaming allowances at lm and jk. Add also a wiring allowance of bare four wire diameters around feabhm, and a single throw-off around kfcdgl to which the bottom is afterwards peined and finally "knocked-up"

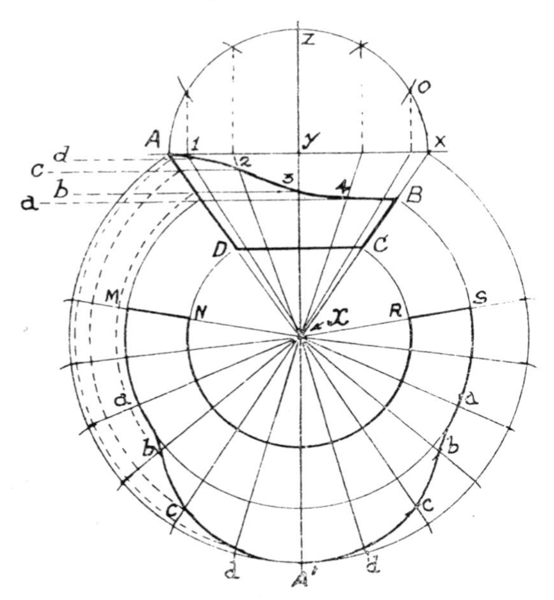

A, D, C, B is the elevation of jug top. Produce A D and B C to intersect at x. Produce side B C to X. Draw A X parallel to D C. With y centre, describe arc A Z X. Divide into six equal parts (half radii), drop perpendiculars to cut A X and draw radii to x. With x centre, describe arcs on C B and X on which step off (each side of centre line xA1) six spaces as OX (top arc). From points of intersection of jug contour with radii 1 2 3 4 (top), draw lines d, c, b, a parallel to AX and cutting A D at d, c, b, a. With these points as radii describe arcs cutting the lower radii at d, c, b, a, each side of centre A. Join these points and the required pattern is N, M, A, S, R, point A being the spout. Add for wire, etc.

Fig. 24.—Pattern for jug top

as explained in Chapter V. The lower sketch D is for a slow taper job and is done exactly as the one above, and so needs no explanation. Such may be used for a square metal jug or the like.

Conical Work—Jug Tops (Pattern Development)

The combined tops and spouts of hot-water jugs may be looked upon as being of conical formation.

Such a pattern is graphically arrived at by the method shown in Fig. 24.

I have purposely included the relevant "text" direct to the sketch for easier reference.

Fig. 25 deals with the same subject, but while the first one is orthodox, or at least pretty generally used, it provides

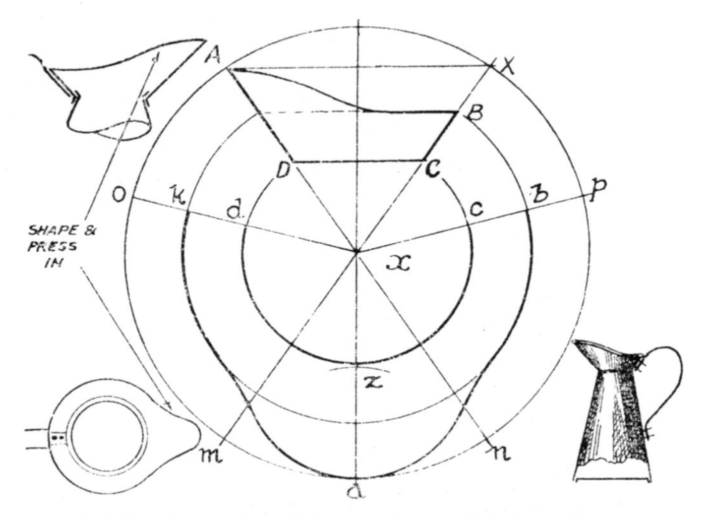

A, D, C, B is the elevation of jug top and spout. This is considered as being a conical form with part of base cut away. Re-form this by producing C B to X, giving A D C X, which, produced to intersect at y, shows a true cone. Describe arcs through C B and X. Produce sides A D, X C through centre x to m, n. Lay off m, n at o, p. Join o x and x p giving the cone pattern o m n p. Draw centre line a x. A and a being the highest points of jug top. Using radius x c strike arc z on centre-line, a x. Strike arc from a to cut m x, n x, at f h. Join freehand to arc b k and d, k, a, b, c is pattern

Fig. 25.—Pattern for jug top (alternative method)

rather a wide spout, which does not look nice, even if considerably squeezed in. Fig. 25—my own particular pride and joy—though possibly less formal looking than its orthodox partner, is equally effective, far quicker to get out and provides a smoother curve at the spout part. As the spout curve is worked from the same radius as the neck-fitting, each spout is automatically in certain proportion to each particular jug.

Some people, when making a jug, fit the spout part into the jug body and solder inside. I prefer the opposite way, and fit the body part into the spout or top. This procedure is shown inset in Fig. 25.

Reverting to this figure for a moment, it will be seen that the jug top itself is part of a cone—a piece cut away. Well, **build it up again and develop therefrom an ordinary conical** pattern for the narrowest part, bringing the actual spout portion out to coincide with the circle drawn through the extreme lip of the spout. This could not be simpler to do and, as before mentioned, gives a better curve and similar dimensions elsewhere.

Working Methods

The actual working-up methods for conical forms is so very similar to those used for bowls and cylindrical work that little need be said about them at this point. One or two specific cases are shown later when it will be seen how closely such procedures resemble one another.

One point in particular calls for notice. A wired edge round a " blunt " cone is rather more difficult to produce than one on either a slow tapering body or a cylinder. It is more like wiring a disc, but with the difference that in wiring a cone backwards the actual turned-back edge has to be stretched and then compressed as in the case of a disc. Fig. 23 will make this clear. Apart from this, I experience very little difference between cones or cylinders. For the benefit of those who may not be conversant with hand methods, cones are perfectly simple to work to shape on any bench bar, mandrel, length of gas main or large piece of shafting. I make great use of such odd pieces—they come cheap, being left-overs from outside jobs, and are of various diameters so that one is easily fixed up for " size."

Fix such a length, say 36 in., on the bench with a strap as for bench mandrel, and allow enough to overhang so as to give plenty of working length. Lay the cone " blank " over the improvised mandrel with the " large end " nearest the bench ; bend one edge down a little over the bar. Then do the same at the opposite end, a bit farther in again at that end and a similar amount at the other. You now have a bent sheet similar to Fig. 23, stages 1 to 4. Taking that sheet in the hands again, gently work it over the bench-bar from centre, each way, forming the " cone " by working the broad end through a wider arc than the other end. It is perfectly possible to make a cone by this method so that hardly an uneven spot is noticeable. It is actually just a case of sliding the work over the bar, taking care that the broad end slides farther, and through a broader arc than the small end.

The photograph of the double-conical old Cornish " tin " pitcher is an example of hand-worked cones. Incidentally this " tin " pitcher happens to be of " copper," tinned inside, of course. It is about 10 in. high and was made as an ornament, but is handy for many purposes.

CHAPTER X

PIPES, PATTERNS AND JOINTS

SHEET metal ventilating or stove pipes may at some time or another be brought to be replaced and copied. These may be either of ordinary black iron sheet or they may be specified in galvanised. The gauge used will be round about 24 to 22, which, though not unduly thick, will be found to have ample stiffness for the usual run of work of this nature. Oil-stove vents may be 26 gauge.

Making up the actual pipe will present but little difficulty to the average general sheet-metal practitioner. It is made up just like a long canister or cylinder. Measure the girth of the pipe, determine in your mind the size of seam to use and whether it is to be just a plain " lap and rivet " or a grooved (hooked) seam. Add this allowance to the girth and carry on rounding up.

Those fortunate enough (or " go-ahead " enough) may possess a set of bending rolls.

These look something like a starved domestic mangle with an extra roller. The extra one is removable to allow the rolled-up sheet to be readily removed. One pair has a series of grooves turned at one end to accommodate any wired edges that may be necessary, and the drivers are so geared together that the work rotates similarly to that done in jennies or beading machines.

You will have to fold back the hooked edges first and then roll so far in the machine and come back over.

When nearly circular, hook up the joint, run a long mandrel piece of shaft, or cast iron or galvanised pipe through it, and rig up on bench similarly to Fig. 30G.

With the mandrel supported at both ends as shown, you can hammer away as much as you like—the bar cannot slew all over the place as it is likely to do otherwise, and in the case of a long bar, this outer crutch gadget takes the strain off the bench.

A good idea is to fill the pipe with water and plug the ends. Or, again, sand is pretty good and makes a really dead mandrel besides taking the "ring" out of it.

In connection with this "water-mandrel" the casual wooden bung (dry-wood to start with, so that it will swell when wet) is all right up to a point. On the other hand, it may come out at some unexpected moment. A drop of water does not hurt, but it makes a nasty mess and the less water in any workshop the better.

If you can weld or know someone who can, weld a ¼ in. or 5/16 in. plate into each end. Drill one end, tap out ¼ in. iron gas and screw a plug in after filling with water.

To resume—the pipe part is finished; now for the elbow part of it.

One way to do the job—some may call it a "sloppy" way—is to make up your pair of pipes the exact length over the corner of the elbow and, starting exactly opposite the seam, cut down diagonally towards the seam with the snips. The Gilbow snips, Fig. 5, are fine for such work. Upon reaching this seam—four metal thicknesses—just nick it through neatly with either a fine hacksaw or a chisel, and file up true. Go on trimming till the joint edge is 45 deg. true on both flanks, taking the seam as centre. Do the other pipe likewise, and then mark around the 45 deg. part a seaming allowance, say for a 5/32 in. seam, that is 5/32 in. on one pipe and a bare ⅜ in. on the other.

Lay the pipes in turn over the mandrel, seam up and file away the groove ridge back to the scribed seam line—5/32 in. on one and bare ⅜ in. on the other. This will allow the edge to be flanged back over. Throw back the ⅜ in. one the full distance marked, and then throw it forward again, as for a can-bottom. Throw off the 5/32 in. one now and offer it up to the other—it should go inside. If not, trim it a little where it fouls, and when it fits, pein down the other part over it and that completes the elbow joint. Be careful where the two seams meet, or you may get a hole.

Another way to arrive at a like result is to work opposite and keep the seams outside. Still another way is to cut the diagonal so that the seams come on opposite sides—not top or bottom. This procedure may take a little more care to ensure that they *are* opposite, but when the peined down joint is made there is less likelihood of a " holiday " or gap at the longitudinal seams. This is quite likely when two grooved seams are joined up with a pared joint—unless considerable care is taken ; hence the suggestion of the left and right seam arrangement cited above—you are paring down on solid metal all round.

If a " holiday " does appear, get your welder-friend to touch the spot.

Pattern Cutting

Having drawn the elbow full size on a stiff piece of brown paper, put in the *base line* 0, 6 (Fig. 26) and from this describe a semi-circle as shown.

Having divided the semi-circle into six, starting at the intersection of centre line with the arc and setting off points 1 and 5, place the compass point on 0 and 6 and set off 2 and 4.

From 0, 1, 2, 3, 4, 5, 6, throw up verticals to cut the diagonal joint-line P6.

The lengths of these resultant lines a, b, c, . . .f, are the main factors in setting out the actual pattern directly below.

This pattern is built up on a line of such length as is known to be more than the circumference of the pipe. Find the approximate centre of it and step off left and right six spaces, as any one of the six half-radii on the semi-circle. From these, throw up further verticals of fair length and from their starting points describe arcs cutting the verticals, such arcs being the lengths a, b, c, . . . f where those letters designate the distance from 0, 6 *base line* to P, 6 *joint line.*

Do each of these in turn, starting with 6 as zero line. The distance a cuts verticals 5. The next dimension, b, cuts the pair of verticals 4, and so on, left and right. The points of intersection of these arcs with the verticals are next

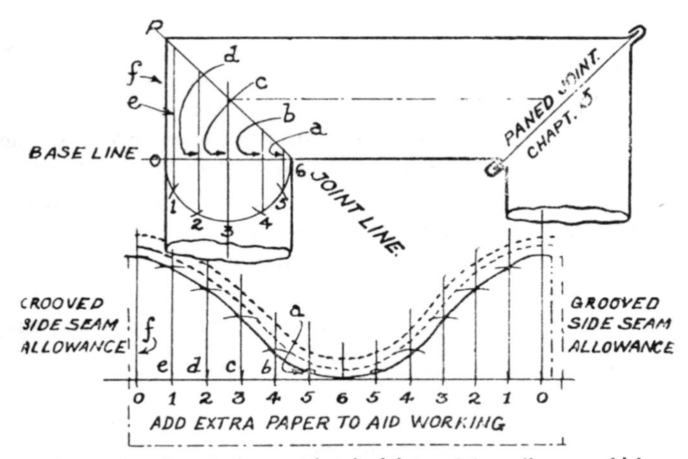

Draw elevation of pipe, putting in joint and base line on which describe arc. Divide into six (half radii) and with compasses step off such sixths each side of a centre on another line drawn below, i.e., pipe circumference. Number as shown and throw up verticals, cutting off on each side of centre 6 to correspond with lines a, b, c, d, e, f measured from base to hypotenuse or joint line, P6, starting with line a at 5, work out to f at 0, joining the arc intersection points with a strong line. The resultant curve is the pattern required. Obtuse angled elbows may be worked up in a similar way

Fig. 26.—Elbows for pipes

joined up with a strong line which denotes the nett dimension for the pattern for a 90 deg. elbow.

Add such jointing allowances as may be desired at the sides, and for the elbow, and then add sufficient underneath to strengthen the pattern at the zero or middle part.

It will, of course, be noted that the longitudinal seam in this case comes on the outsides of the two members.

In this elbow work, whether by the cut and try method, or graphically, care must be taken to provide sufficient length of pipe to make up for the elbow joint.

If it is going to be a 5/32 in. seam allow that on one and near enough $\frac{3}{8}$ in. on the other. It is better to make the two pipes too long and cut off after, than have them too short, though it is not often that stove or vent pipes are worked so exactly as to cause an odd half-inch of extra length to matter.

As stated at the foot of Fig. 26, obtuse angled elbows are similarly treated. The actual working up is easier also, as the " throat " is more get-at-able for peining.

As a last word on this subject, in order to ensure that one pipe will fit into its mate, cut the sheets just a 3/32 in. either full or bare at one end. A distance of 3/32 in. on the circumference is about 1/32 in. on diameter and that usually does the trick nicely. You can also expand the end on the mandrel or pipe stake by hammering all round for an inch or two up the pipe. but be careful not to over-do this, or you may have a surprise—and a sloppy fit.

Pipe Expanding

This hammering treatment will enable one to expand a pipe—a solid-drawn pipe—to quite a large degree

In the thicker and larger gauges and diameters, such as brass, copper, or aluminium tubes may be hammered " taper " to as much as $\frac{1}{2}$ in. larger at one end on a 3 in. or 4 in. diameter, on, again, lengths of from an inch to a foot or more ; anyway, as long as may be convenient to put on a pipe stake or mandrel.

Place the tube on the stake, chalk or scratch a line lengthways and proceed to hammer with a flat-faced planishing hammer. Actually, any $\frac{3}{4}$ or 1 pound hammer will do as long as its face is good. Strike successive rings of blows all round, increasing the power of blows as you proceed along the pipe with these rings. Watch the diameter. Start the second round, say, about $\frac{3}{4}$ in. or 1 in. further along and carry on towards the end, keeping in fairly well-defined rings all the way along. Start the third visitation about $1\frac{1}{2}$ in. from the end, and the fourth another $\frac{3}{4}$ in. or so from that again—and so on, until the pipe has the required amount of taper.

A brazed-up tube is very liable to split under this treatment, even when annealed, and it is not always easy to distinguish a solid drawn pipe or tube from that of the brazed variety. The seam is not always obvious on the outside and it may be so well done that it is not much in evidence inside either. Rub a file—a smooth file—over the end and close examination will disclose a pinkish line through the metal. This line sometimes denotes a butt join or a scarpled (thinned off lap) join, and if such is present expansion will be performed at the worker's own risk—it is almost bound to split.

To anneal copper sheet or pipe, use a forge fire or blow-lamp, heat to blood red, quench out in water and mind your eyes. For brass, use similar heating and allow to cool off on its own.

When so treating a copper pipe that is only to be heated part way, be careful when quenching to hold the cold end in tongs, otherwise that " cold " end is going to burn your hands, if the pipe is only about a couple of feet long. On quenching, the heat immediately leaves the dipped end (obviously) but it flashes along the unheated portion at such a rate that if one has more than a few paces to go with it after a quick cool it will become so " heavy " that one drops it like a ton weight. Asbestos gloves can be obtained, and these will be found a godsend for handling hot metal, saving many a nasty burn.

Utilising Scrap Pipe or Tube

If you happen to run short of thick sheet copper-plate for a job that needs a hefty patch or gusset-plate, or even a pipe clip—in fact, anything at all in that line—just pick out of the scrap box a piece of old copper exhaust pipe. Cut, say, six inches off (bulges do not matter), grip it fairly tightly in the vice and saw through one side as far as the middle, using the saw so that it does not cut the opposite side—the under-part. Then cut through the other end, going easily when the remainder nips the saw. Wedge the cut open with a couple of stout screw drivers or cold chisels until a couple of pairs of gas pliers will enter. Open up, hammer out flat, anneal and there is a very handy piece of sheet metal. You can do brass as well, but anneal this both before and after cutting open.

CHAPTER XI

PLANISHING

In making up sheet metal ware the worker is very fortunate if he can go for long without coming across a " buckled " piece.

As purchased in fair bulk—say 1 cwt. at a time—it may be supplied packed either in a crate, or anyhow with a board backing. Such sheets are generally a stock size of four feet by two feet. Beautifully smooth in bulk, as soon as they have been pulled around a bit, cut into and thrust back into the rack, there comes a time when some job one is on refuses to lie flat.

The commonest offender is the round sheet which evinces an irrepressible desire to rise in the middle. You press it down and out it goes the other way. It will spin like a top if given a twist. To the uninitiated, the most appropriate procedure is to beat the middle with a hammer or a mallet—generally the hammer because it is harder—and they look quite surprised, when the thing plops in and out and spins worse than ever.

In this planishing now, the main step is to diagnose the trouble—literally put your fingers on it (and all over it) and get it to tell you why it is so uncomfortable. Take it in your hands and " feel " it. Lay it flat on the bench or surface plate and feel it again. Watch it as you take your hands away and its action will guide you like the symptoms of disease. Press it in one place and it will twitch in another. Keep that part so it cannot move and (in very bad cases) it will give a " plop " somewhere else, and so you go on, concentrating on the why and wherefore until the trouble is fixed. Metal can talk in its own way to one who understands but a little of its language. That understanding and "feel" is half the battle with metal working—either sheet or "bulk."

Fig. 27A, page 97, shows a cut disc. The trouble is that it will not lie flat; merely to hit it with a hammer in the middle makes matters far worse. Whereabouts on the surface does this tendency to rise begin or end? The edges seem even enough, but the middle flops in and out from, say, 2 or 3 in. inwards from the edge.

The "feel" of it shows that somehow or other the middle part is too big for the surrounding "zone" and that is exactly the trouble.

Place it upon a flat iron surface plate, or upon the planishing anvil, shown in the sketch, clean the face of your mallet with a file so as to make it slightly convex and then from that circle where the trouble seems to begin, strike a ring of contiguous blows—not too hard—all round that part.

Now feel the job. Very likely the floppiness, or "looseness" as it is generally known, has dispersed and covers a wider area; and possibly its degree is less noticeable.

Run round another circle of blows outside the first, and feel again. Carry on with this treatment, feeling now and then to find how things are progressing.

In a short time, no doubt that sheet will lie flat as a pancake on the surface plate, comfortable and easy—because you have eased its outer bonds and allowed its mid-portion room to lie flat. Before, it could not; that part *had* to go somewhere, so it went upwards or downwards, but it could not stretch itself out. The cause for its being "edge-bound" was no doubt the action of cutting the disc. The edge metal became compressed. No amount of indiscriminate hammering would fix it. One or two wrong blows would take perhaps twenty others correctly placed to counteract such bad effect.

Having cured the circular patient with the "loose" centre

we will next attend to the square or rectangular one, which appears to suffer the same or very like trouble.

A word about these sketches, however. Those numerous little rings are not supposed to denote that hammer marks are to be visible over the work. They are merely to show very definitely just where the blows are to be delivered, or rather from where and in which direction they are to go. The hammer, if and where used, may be just an ordinary $\frac{3}{4}$ or 1 lb. engineer's type, but the face must be dressed up perfectly smooth and kept emery clothed one way in prolongation with the shaft or handle. If any grit, small hairs or other foreign bodies are permitted to adhere thereto, each and every one will leave its impression in the metal worked on. Generally speaking, I use a hammer for planishing, and keep it for nothing else; always emery cloth it before and during use. The importance of keeping a hammer clean has already been stressed.

In sketch B, it will be noticed that the edge is, like that previous, " tight " ; but being " square " very possibly may be a little more difficult.

In the first case the " looseness " is more definitely located. The " tight " edge is perhaps as evenly defined as the sketch. It is often possible to locate the actual " loose " portion as near as a $\frac{1}{4}$ in. one way or the other. It can definitely be placed by " feel." Lay the sheet on the surface plate and press it with a finger, carefully noting exactly the area which moves when pressure is brought to bear upon it ; also the visible effect when the pressure is released.

Generally, a few light blows on the borders of the tight part will show what the effect is going to be. Should they improve matters noticeably, carry on another couple of rounds with the same weight of blow, when examination will show whether to proceed with that weight or whether, in the worker's opinion, he should hit a bit harder.

Should the first tentative blows (shown within the loose

centre in B) have done more harm than good it may be taken as a warning to start work well on the other side of that imaginary border line, and moreover, to hit pretty hard.

Work outwards as denoted by the arrows, increasing the strength of the blows in that direction as you proceed. At the same time keep the sheet rotating slowly under the hammer.

Feel the sheet from time to time, and if there is a tendency to flop at the edges, ease up a little on the hammering, or the exact reverse condition may occur—the edges may grow so that they are pulled by the centre. If that happens, revert to those tentative blows within the boundary lines ; a few mallet blows hereabouts should even things up, when possibly the final planishing towards the outer sides may be carried out with the mallet.

There is no hard and fast rule about this planishing procedure. The workman has to visualise exactly what the trouble is and do his best to rectify it. Should he go adrift either with his diagnosis or his treatment, he must try again. There is one thing about it : he can always rectify his errors whilst the work remains " in the flat " that is, un-made-up. This subsequent rectification may take more time, but with patience and thought there are few cases that cannot be fixed satisfactorily.

Case C is exactly the opposite to A. The edge wobbles up and down in waves. One side may be " up " and a nearby part may be " down." While examining it, some other part of the edge will suddenly give a flip one way or another.

This denotes that the centre part is too small and is dragging the edge. The centre is " tight " and the edge " loose."

Careful examination, again, should reveal just where the tightness and looseness begin and end.

Leave a central area, say 2 in. diameter, quite untouched and begin hammering from what may be termed the

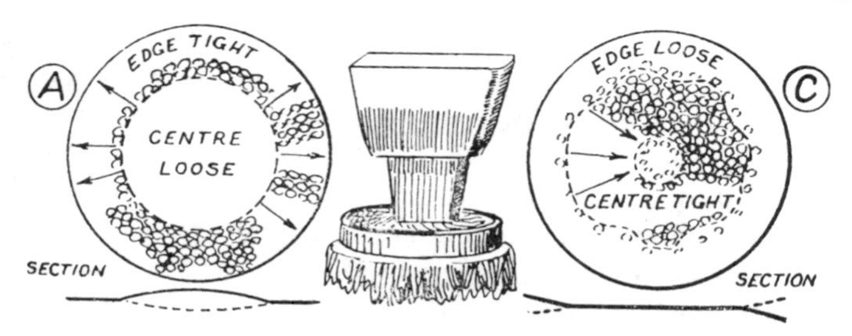

Planish tight parts of A and B, C and D, as indicated by arrows

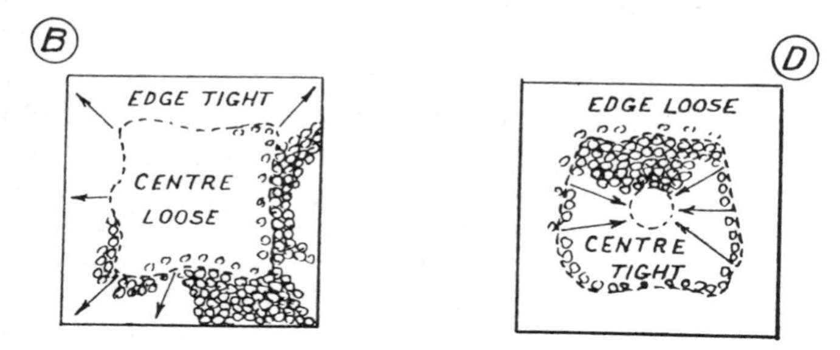

Planishing centres in cases like C, D, E must be avoided if possible or loose centre may result

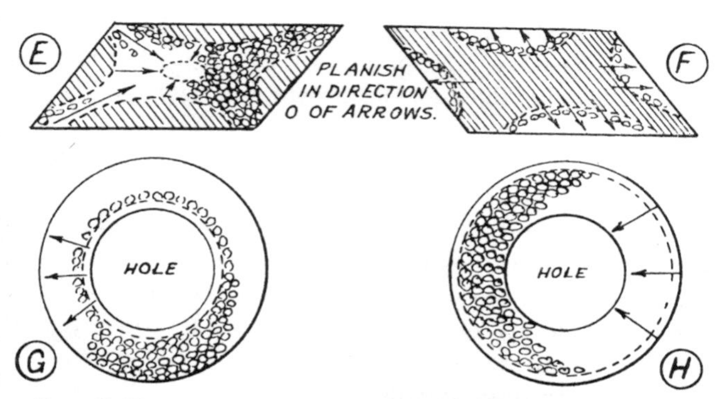

Treat G, H as A and C. Except for hole, cases are identical. For G, work outward from dotted circle. For H, work inward from dotted circle

Fig. 27.—Planishing

" neutral " line inwards, slightly increasing the power and closeness of the blows towards that 2 in. centre that is " taboo." It is out of bounds—except as a last resource.

Such hammering may be done in radial lines inwards, (meanwhile moving the sheet round to suit the workman's position or comfort) or the blows may equally well be struck in concentric circles decreasing in diameter as the " taboo " centre is approached, again moving the sheet to suit. Comfortable position of the sheet relative to the movement of the arm and body is everything. One cannot place a blow just where desired if the body or arm is " out of focus," to use a somewhat mixed metaphor.

Should this treatment prove too much of a good thing and the work develop the trouble as in A or B, give the outer part that was once " loose " a quick, light working-over with the mallet and everything should be all right.

The trouble in D is similar to C. The edge is all over the place and will not stay in one plane.

Treat as for previous one, from neutral line inwards in direction of arrows, all round. If overdone, lightly mallet the edge and try again.

In really obstinate cases one may even have to enter the " taboo " centre. If so, go very easy with the hammering. The less hammer at the centre, the less likelihood of a big spot of trouble.

It is my considered opinion that this centre part should never be touched except as a very last resource and, perhaps, not even then. At any rate, think it over carefully first.

The sketch E brings up a case where certain well-defined parts of a sheet are light and loose. The cross-hatched portions are floppy or wavy, which will, by this time, be recognised as meaning " loose."

The tight, or dragging part is thus formed like a cross. It may extend diagonally or may be " square " across from the middle of each side. The treatments are similar. Start from the outer extremities of each tight part and carry on towards the not-to-be-touched part. Try the arms of the cross first. It may be that planishing these alone will go a long way towards putting matters right. One can but try, and why go on hammering a lot when by hammering a little and examining a little, much trouble may be saved. Always remember that in planishing, a few blows too many may take many more to rectify.

F is dead opposite to E. The centre part feels like an oil-can bottom—you can push it in and out. The outer corners also seem willing to follow suit, but the sides feel rigid and under tension. They also may move about a little, but only because their area is very small compared with the loose or floppy areas. They must more or less conform to public opinion as it were, but by means of passive resistance cause quite a bit of unrest to the whole, and so there is a great shaded area upset by those four small mid-side portions. Lay the work on the anvil or plate and hammer them as shown—an arc of blows in each sector at a time—and watch the effect as progress is made.

By degrees the main portion should assume a normal position.

If the edges just done develop a loose tendency, take the mallet and give each corner of the plate (say an area 2 in. × 2 in.) a few moderate mallet blows, and all should be well.

Sketches G and H are identical with A and C except for the presence of the hole. The cause of the looseness of the inner edge may be the method used in cutting out the centre.

Should a chisel have been used, this will set up complications within the metal at that part, compressing the metal around the cut edge. It cannot spread outwards as it is bounded by the rest of the metal ring, and so must either go up or down.

Treat this as A and planish towards outer edge either radially all round or in concentric circles of blows.

H is treated similarly to C, and for the same reason. There remain a few unillustrated cases of metal sheets that have wired edges and suffer from troubles similar to these cited.

For example, if A had a wired outer edge it could not be planished farther than the wire. The expanded metal would still be edge-bound, so in that case such a job where practicable would be put through the jenny and treated as is the wired disc illustrated in Fig. 18. The face of the wired disc is pressed back until it is level or nearly level with the back edge of wiring. This procedure tends to stretch the metal away from the centre, which is to all intents equivalent to giving it a larger area.

Should the wire be round the inner edge of the hole, similar treatment may be given, though not by mechanical means. Lay the work on the surface plate or other wide face and, with a flat-faced punch, gently knock back the face metal until it nearly or actually does touch the plate.

If the work has a double wiring (*i.e.*, outer and inner edges and centre part between " loose " or " floppy ") do not use the hammer at all. Work back both the faces which are contiguous to the wired edges ; this should stretch, or rather " allow " the middle of the ring somewhere to go.

Much of the planishing art simply cannot be lucidly put into words. The whole thing is rather simple when you can actually feel where the trouble lies, and, as said at the outset, given the patience and a certain sensitivity of touch or feel, the piece of metal should just about " talk " to you.

CHAPTER XII

RIVETING

Tools

THE tools used for riveting sheet metal need not be elaborate. Suitable tackle for this work may be obtained from all tool dealers of repute, but such tools are of standard type and offer but little chance for the discriminating (or as usually considered—"finicky") purchaser who has ideas of his own about the exact size or type of tool he requires.

In Fig. 28 is a group of riveting tools—sets, snaps and hold-ups, clamps, etc.

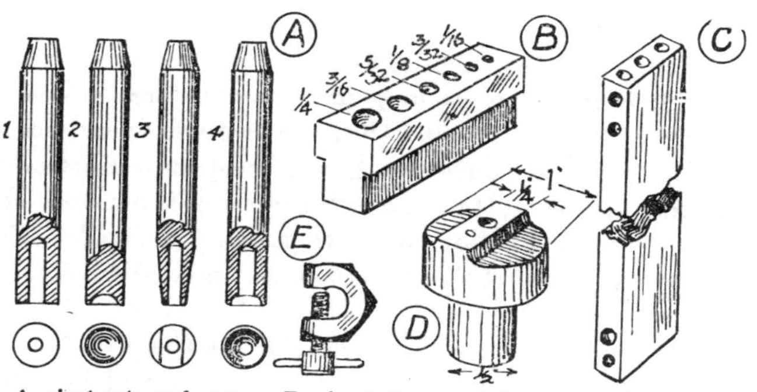

A, rivet sets and snaps. B, vice hold-up. C, Long reach hold-up for inside work (may be used vertically or horizontally). D, hold-up for bar or anvil

Fig. 28.—Rivet sets, "hold-ups" etc.

These materials, altogether, did not cost more than two shillings and they have served finely over a period of many years. There may be many local terms for these tools, but they are referred to here by names which are generally used.

The group of punches at A is divided into "sets" and "snaps."

The first is a "set," sometimes also spelt "sett." This tool is, in the case shown, made of $\frac{1}{2}$ in. mild steel round rod.

It is placed over the protruding rivet shank and used to "set" or close home the two sheets tightly, as well as to settle the rivet head snugly against the metal. The central hole is drilled up by any suitable means. I use a lathe for the purpose and cut off in the next operation, though the work may equally well be done in the vice with a hand-drill. This hole should be long enough to take the longest rivet likely to be used in any particular size, the diameter being an easy fit over the rivet.

The second from the left is a "snap," and this is for forming and finally closing the edges of the formed head snugly down upon the sheet metal.

The hollow end should be made truly hemispherical—semicircular on section. They rarely are as accurately made, however, and as long as they are pretty nearly a good copy of the rivet head they are as good as is necessary. The depth of the concavity should be just a fraction less than the height of the formed head on the rivet, so as not to dig into the sheet metal when using the tool. These, also, may be made of a like diameter of mild steel—recessed in the lathe.

The third one is a "set" similar to the first. It has a pair of flats, filed upon opposite sides, which narrows the working surface so that it can be placed easily between closely-spaced rivets. Also it enables the user to operate close up to a flange or shoulder or the side of a vessel during construction.

The fourth tool is a special "set" for drawing up a head of a rivet into the sheet metal, or more correctly for simultaneously forming a cup in the sheet-metal and drawing the rivet head up into it, thus giving a flush surface on that side. It makes a stronger job than a countersunk hole in the metal would do.

Suppose, for example, that a couple of 1/32 in. sheets—or 20 s.w.g., near enough—had to be riveted flush on one side. By the time that side had been countersunk, either 60 or 45 deg. angle, there would be precious little metal left for holding, and even the knife-edge of that would be badly deformed by the actual riveting. So, having drilled the appropriate size hole, this set will draw the head up into a cup formed of two metal thicknesses which may be seen in Fig. 30, E and d^1.

All these tools should be made up some time or another until a range of sizes from 1/16 in. to ¼ in. is obtained. In the smaller sizes up to ⅛ in. the stock may be from ¼ in. to ⅜ in. diameter, the size for ¼ in. shank rivets could, with advantage, be as heavy as ¾ in.

Sketch B is what may be termed a " hold-up "—a term that exactly describes its job. Two or more pieces have to be riveted together with " snap " heads. Nothing looks worse than snap or round heads that have been laid on a flat face for the heading-up process. This vice hold-up may be some 3 in. long and, say, ¾ in. wide on face, the vice tenon planed, filed, or sawn out. Mild steel may be used in its normal condition, but as one of these things takes some time to make, once made it pays to keep it in condition, so have it case hardened.

The hold-up may, with advantage, be made of tool steel and then hardened and drawn back to dark straw or purple. Place it in the forge fire, bring it to blood red heat and swill it round in a bucket of water, keeping it there till cold. Rub up the face on emery cloth and lay face-up on a big, red-hot iron until the face turns dark straw or purple, and quench out again.

Another way is to heat up to redness, quench the face only for a ¼ in. depth, quickly rub it over a sandstone block until fairly bright and watch the remaining heat travel back into the face again until the desired straw colour or purple is visible ; then quench right out in cold water.

The little " head " D is for a like purpose, but mainly for inside work. The top is filed away each side of the recess so that it may be located between closely-spaced rivet heads. It has a rivet head impression in its face and also, it will be noted, a " shank " sized hole so that it can also be used as an upside-down set, with an ordinary snap to close up a particular type of job in which, perhaps, that method is the easier. This fits into an anvil " punch " hole. Sketch C is of a long bar—maybe 10 in. to 20 in. long by an end section of $\frac{3}{8}$ in. $\times$ 1 in. up to $\frac{3}{4}$ in. $\times$ 2 in. It has rivet head impressions at each end and at the edges also. These are for a range of sizes, the bar being used inside jobs for holding up where other means are impossible. It may be used vertically or horizontally.

One example of its use is for riveting the filling cap flange on to a tank before the bottom or end is fitted. Or again, inside a can for holding up rivets to secure the handle ; in fact for no particular purpose but for every case where it may be used to advantage.

The little clamp may be made up out of a $\frac{1}{2}$ in. or $\frac{5}{8}$ in. machine nut. It may, again, be cut from solid nearly as quickly. It need not be that particular shape. Just cut a square piece of steel off a bar or " flat," poke a $\frac{1}{2}$ in. or a $\frac{5}{8}$ in. drill through and another 13/64 in. crossways to tap $\frac{1}{4}$ in. for the screw. Slit through the side of the large hole with hacksaw and file up to any outline desired.

These small clamps are invaluable for holding jobs in place while marking off rivet holes, and while actually riveting or soldering. They are cheap to make and prevent a lot of " slipping " at inopportune moments.

In Fig. 29 is shown, in side section, plan and end section, a small gadget that I use when a good many closely-spaced rivets have to be marked out, punched, and drilled.

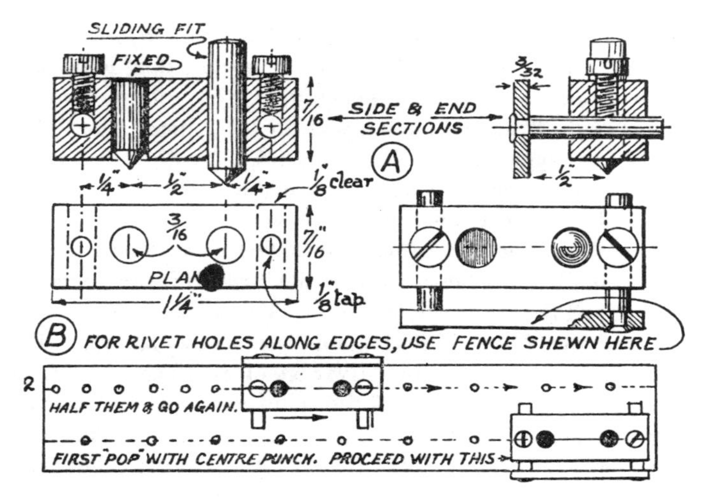

Below.—For punching diagonal lines of rivet holes remove fence and use block against straight-edge

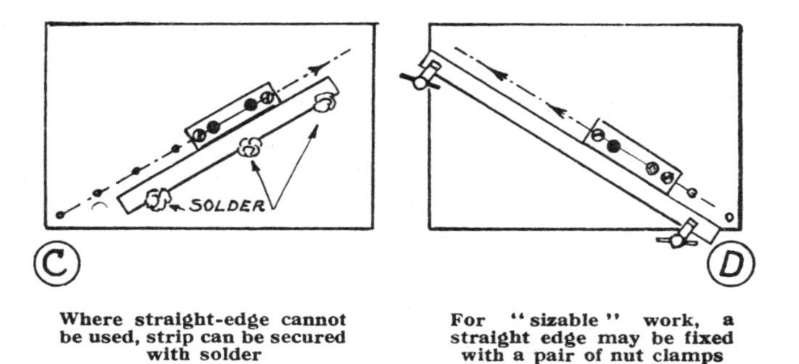

Where straight-edge cannot be used, strip can be secured with solder

For "sizable" work, a straight edge may be fixed with a pair of nut clamps

Fig. 29.—Hole spacing punch

Of course, it does not pay (financially, anyway) to make such a thing unless there is a fair number of holes to space, but when this was first evolved I had a job where about twelve hundred had to be spaced, punched, drilled, arris cleaned off, rivets inserted, held up, headed and snapped.

Spacing had to be meticulously correct and after tentatively playing round with dividers for a while, this idea was schemed out. The actual spacing of the job mentioned was 7/32 in. The tool shown will do $\frac{1}{4}$ in. spacing or $\frac{1}{2}$ in., used at the one setting. It is simplicity itself. On a plain piece of steel, cast iron or gunmetal, mark off centre lines and drill the two main punch and spacing point holes 3/16 in. Drill two more outside the first pair, either $\frac{1}{8}$ in. or 5/32 in. These are for the arms of the fence to slide through. Down into these drill a pair of 7/64 in. holes and tap $\frac{1}{8}$ in. Whit. for small setscrews shown. The " start point " is 3/16 in. silver steel hardened to straw colour and a drive fit so that the point comes about 1/32 in. below the face of the tool. The long " punch " is slidable, a nice easy fit. The fence speaks for itself. The arms are also a nice fit in either the $\frac{1}{8}$ in. or 5/32 in. cross holes in the block. The setscrews secure them in place at whatever setting the fence is desired. In size shown its major range is $\frac{1}{2}$ in. clear of the punch and its minimum 7/32 in. To use, punch the first mark with an ordinary centre pop. Insert the little space-point therein and, with a light hammer, say 4 oz., drive on the sliding punch-point, gradually sliding the block towards you, the fixed point dropping with a click into the mark just done. The fence keeps the alignment fair with the edge of the sheet. It is easier to work towards one, and on the right side of a sheet. Come down one side, turn the sheet end for end, and come down the opposite side (Fig. 29B).

In the case of a diagonal or centre line of holes too far " in " to use the fence, remove it, fix a straight-edge to the sheet by such means as are convenient, or as suggested in Fig. 29C. Note, however, that such guiding edge must be half the width of the block away from the desired centre line of the rivets.

It is a very handy tool, and you can make it any size you wish. It will do two spacings, one, as made and shown, does ½ in. Now "halve" the first spacing, use as start and come back again at ¼ in. spacing.

Methods

Coming, now, to actual riveting, the type of work most commonly seen is very likely that used in domestic and general utility articles.

Buckets, dustbins, oil stoves and ovens, kitchen ware, and so on, are produced on mass production lines. It would be impossible to mark off, pop and drill for every rivet, so the self-piercing principle is very much in evidence. The rivet is lined up under the material, a descending "set" pushes the metal down over the rivet, and in some cases the heading-up is probably done by a continuation of the motion. Such procedure does not come within the scope of this handbook, but a modification of the same principle is often resorted to in sheet-metal workers' shops. The work is placed over the mandrel or whatever is used as a hold-up, the rivet placed in position and the "set" forced down over it with a good heavy blow of, say, a 1½ lb. hammer. A few skilfully directed blows around the rivet stalk and the snap is applied. A proper tinsmith's "set" has also a "snap" combined therewith so that no time is lost between operations and the set is always in proportion to the snap. This tool very much resembles Fig. 28D, having a long handle or shank about 4 in. long and about ⅝ in. diameter—generally octagonal.

Another point concerning this rivet-driving method, apart from quickness, is that it produces a very snugly fitting rivet. It is a frictional fit all the way and, if neatly and skilfully done, the final snapping operation tends to tighten it further by closing back on to the rivet shank the arris caused by punching. Added to all this, the snapped head makes security still more secure. Galvanising is performed afterwards, which still further tightens things up, and so reliable are the results that it is safe to assert that not one out of, say, fifty buckets or similar vessels is returned as leaky. An ironmonger may save a few of these jobs so that they can all be done at the same "shopping"—a touch of spirits of salts and a little solder over the rivet, a quick wipe off and the job is "new" again.

But because such a method is described here, it must not be supposed that it has my approval, or that it is my usual practice. Carefully marking out and drilling, and as carefully setting and snapping is the rule of the shop. One is "just poking rivets through sheet metal," the other method is "riveting."

Proper riveting is illustrated in Fig. 30. The type of hammer used is one specially made. One face is about $\frac{3}{8}$ in. diameter and the other about 9/32 in., both rounded a little. The weight of this hammer is about $\frac{1}{2}$ lb. It is used for the general run of such work entailing the use of rivets from 1/16 in. to $\frac{1}{4}$ in. diameter. It will also form conical heads, working pretty much as shown in Fig. 30B—but do not strike dead a-top; keep the hammer as shown dotted and work round. These heads are not snapped at all—just left "off the hammer."

Length

This all-important factor is in many cases, judging from observation, entirely ignored or overlooked. Mass-produced pots, pans and buckets, and many other things, seem just to have any length of rivet banged in, and hit anyhow—the result a kind of bent-over, half-head apology passing as a rivet. For average heading my own practice is to allow $1\frac{1}{2}$ in. diameters for small rivets from 1/16 in. to $\frac{1}{8}$ in., a single diameter for those to 3/16 in., and a bare diameter up to $\frac{1}{4}$ in. and over.

This must not be taken as a hard and fast rule or a theoretical allowance, but merely as one man's practice. Some may need a little less because of their tendency to bend their rivets—very few will require more. So by

Using tinman's lead | **Using snap heads**

Anvil or hold-up recessed to fit heads and avoid their distortion

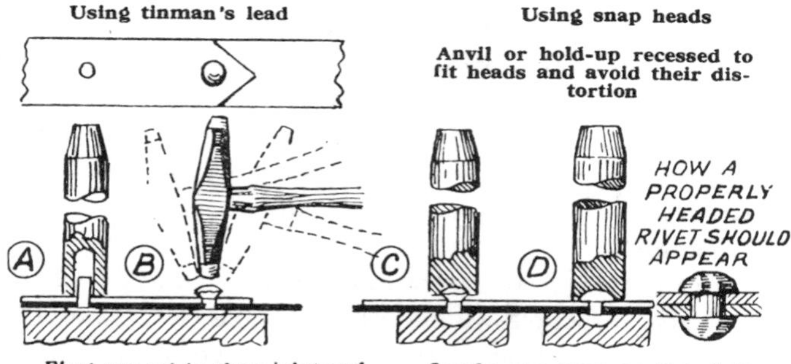

First use set to close joint and settle rivet on anvil. Head up with hammer as in B

Lastly, use snap as C and D

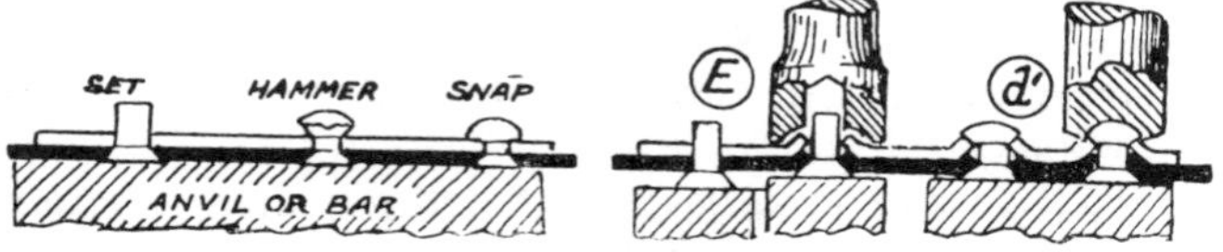

Countersunk rivet

Lower sheet is countersunk for reception of rivet heads. Work is done on a flat face. In some cases left as hammered; in others, snapped

Countersunk rivets used where strength and tightness are desired. The head is drawn up into sheet with hollow ended set, then headed with snap, then "sweated" inside and out

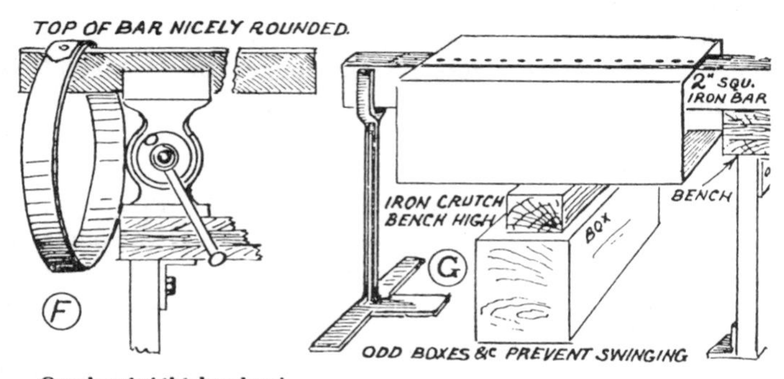

Overhang right-hand end about 18 in. to balance load due to hammering. This decreases strain on vice

Fig. 30.—Simple riveted joints

keeping round about the amounts cited and using care a good head should result; by "good" is meant a full, solid head, not just a "half-baked" burred end.

To get good, consistent riveting "length" must be studied and adhered to. A suitable hammer must be used—from the wrist and not slung from the elbow; and not "any old hammer."

Having got what to appearances may be termed a good head, there are people who don't seem able to "knock off" once they start with the hammer. They go on hammering and snapping, with the result that they so shorten the rivet that it actually crushes the metal between the heads and weakens the lot. Such a rivet, although tight enough at that moment, will not be tight very long—in short, it is a "dud."

As soon as you have made a full head, just an *easy fit and a bit higher than the hollow in the snap*, snap it, and knock off. Any further fiddling will put paid to it. Remember, too, that a dud rivet, knowingly passed, may be the means of even lives being lost. One silly little rivet in an insignificant location may, if it works loose, set up a train of trouble one would give anything to prevent. It sounds like moralising and preaching, but how many ever think of it? "The more rivets in, the bigger the pay-roll" is not always the best way to a quiet conscience.

Types of Rivets

Consider now stages A and B in Fig. 30. *Tinner's flat-headed* rivets are used. Holes are suitably drilled, rivets cut to length described and shown, and headed and snapped.

Snap-head rivets are used in C, D, in which cases such a "hold-up" as B or D, Fig. 28, is used to accommodate the heads underneath while the tops are headed up and snapped.

Ordinary *Countersunk* rivets are shown directly under A and B. Holes are drilled and countersunk for reception

Example of rivet spacing using spacing punch shown in Fig. 29. More than 1,200 1/16 in. rivets are spaced at 7/32 in. centres of heads, which are then held up on a flat anvil or plate while being headed up. They may also be double-countersunk; that is, riveted into a top countersink as well. On fairly thick material, say from 18 s.w.g. upwards, such rivets give very fair strength. Below this thickness such rivets tend to work loose, as the countersunk and thinned inner edges of the holes are likely to distort under riveting and more or less pull through. Where practicable, as with brass or copper or similar metal, one can reinforce with a sweated solder joint.

Where a joint practically as strong as is given by double-headed rivets is desired, together with one flush face, the method shown in Fig. 30, E and d^1, is quite effective.

Drill to size, enter the rivet and drive down over it the cup-headed set shown. The result is also depicted; the metals rising into this cup-head and allowing the rivet to enbed its head flush with the underside sheet. Viewed from the top surface, the rivet hole appears also countersunk now, although just ordinarily drilled at the start. Its edges are 45 deg. a side as at E, this being caused by the stretching of the metal round the hole by the upward thrust of the head underneath when the metal was driven down with the hollow set. Subsequent and careful hammer treatment causes the rivet, now cut to length, to fill the V-shaped orifice and also to form a fair head; this is finished with snap which finishes off the rounded head and caulks down the edges of the head and also caulks the edges of the volcano-like protuberance even more tightly against the rivet head. Run a film of solder round on both sides and there is a joint that will stay put—it has been used many times on fuel tanks, which form a pretty severe test.

Holding-up

Not every job can be held conveniently on an anvil or a vice hold-up. Take a long job, such as the tank shown at G, and compare it with the hoop or band hanging over the vice-bar at F. Even if one overhung a bench-mandrel to such an extent as, say, two-thirds of a tank's length, there would be quite a bit of leverage imposed on the bench top and fixings.

So in order to do such a tank comfortably the bar is best used at such a length as will be about 6 in. clear at the outer end of the work. Support this end on a crutch as shown, and you may hammer as much and as long as you like. The bar or mandrel cannot shift about, nor can the work overbalance it. No strain of note is imparted to the bench. With a central seam such a job will hang normal, but should the seam be near or at a corner, the tank will have to be supported so that it cannot swing. This is easily effected by one or two old boxes or the like packed up until they will just comfortably slide under the work when suspended level. Should noise be for some reason " out of order " a " quietener " in the form of an old sack may be thrown over that portion of the job not worked upon at the moment.

End Riveting " Hold-ups "

Fig. 31A shows a rig-up that I have used once or twice on big work. 36 in. × 24 in. × 10 in. is big when it has to be done by one man.

The ends were in-set about $\frac{3}{4}$ in. and riveted. Strengthening the ends, or at least making for further rigidity, were beaded grooves (not shown) pressed inwards against which the ends were forced and secured in place.

The edges were tinned before this and thoroughly sweated afterwards—rivets as well. (See Chapters XIII, XV.)

The actual problem was to be able to move such a tank about easily, while preserving its level so that it would sit fair on the anvil hold-up. A tank of such size in 18 gauge brass, with anti-surging partitions, weighs nearly half a hundredweight, and would have to be pushed about to and fro a hundred or more times. The solution was an old roller skate nailed to a board and packed up so that the tank was horizontal. Of course, with inside-edge riveting, as one came to the narrow sides one had to turn the tank up on edge, which meant that the anvil and the whole job became too high to manipulate on the bench. It was 2 ft. above that, and near enough neck-high, so it was relegated to the floor—it, and all its retinue—and finished on a more lowly plane. For any such job where the convenient acquisition of a roller skate is out of the question, use four slices of " fat " curtain pole, or borrow the kiddie's toy engine or wooden horse wheels, anything circular and of convenient size—ball races, for example. Nail these to a piece of wood as inset sketch A. With fortune, possibly a kiddies' truck may be available on loan in return for a copper or so. All this may seem highly comical, but I would seriously like to know how else such a job can be conveniently accomplished? Lifting a cumbersome fifty pounds every few moments is no light work.

Sketch B shows how a circular tank was riveted at the ends. It was larger, as will be noted. The rivet holes were drilled by still another fancy rig-up which is shown in Fig. 39. A pair of ball races were bolted to a piece of tee-section iron bar, the middle portion of which was sawn out so that the tank would not foul it, and the job was just rolled from one rivet hole to the next as easily as shelling peas. The little hold-up head fitted the punching hole in the anvil and was very similar to the one shown in Fig. 28D. The flanks being cut away accommodated the adjacent rivet head, the one being headed reposing snugly in the recess in the hold-up. The job was done with something like " elegance " and both jobs were done by the same roller device.

Reverting to A for a moment, the anti-surging partitions or bulkheads in the middle were put in with the edges facing the same way as each respective end. The anvil just reached—in fact their location was, in this case, subjected to the length of the anvil.

Should a definite spacing have been imperative and have been so that the anvil would not reach far enough inwards, a thick iron bar laid along the anvil face, and securely tied each side of the anvil body, would have done the trick very well. The cord fixing at the " flat " end would have come clear of the tank anyway. As for balance—perhaps the bar would have been just right to balance itself. If a short one, and overhung a lot (to reach) a block of lead at the other end of the anvil would have done that. The

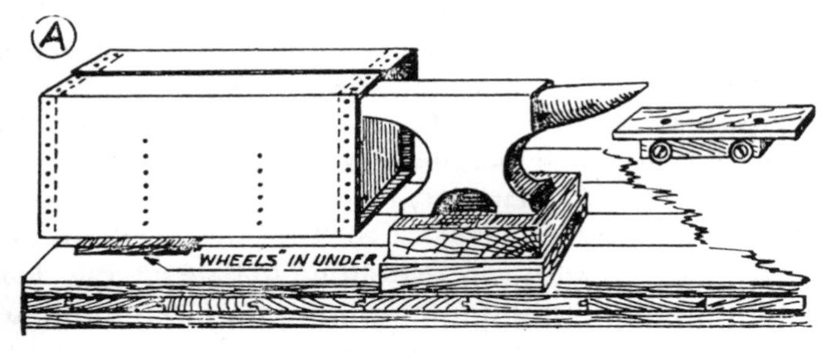

Tank about 36 in. long, 24 in. wide and 10 in. deep. Two partitions inside.

Ends inset ¾ in. and riveted 1 in. centres. Balance and easy-mobility obtained on old roller skate nailed to board on which tank lay. Pushed back as rivets were located on anvil hold-up, working from far side. (Easier working towards than away from one)

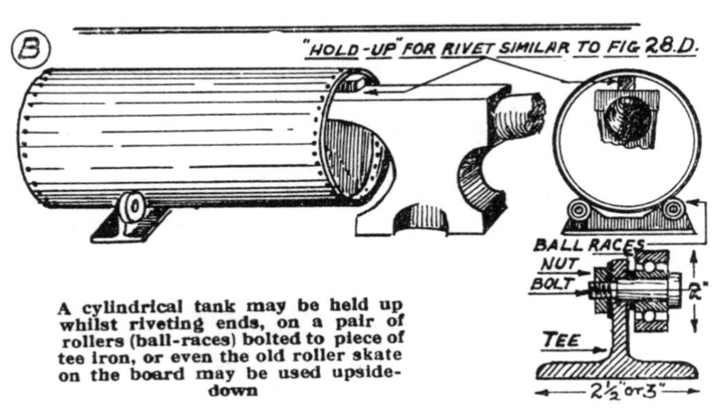

A cylindrical tank may be held up whilst riveting ends, on a pair of rollers (ball-races) bolted to piece of tee iron, or even the old roller skate on the board may be used upside-down

Fig. 31.—Single-handed hold-ups (mainly for large work)

same applies to the round tank—bar tied to anvil and a hole for the little hold-up head or block drilled in the end.

It must not be supposed that the methods referred to or described herein are the only ones. There are many other types of rivets used throughout the various branches of industry. Some heads are spun with rotary "snaps," others are formed by rotary rollers, that is they rotate on spindles or adapters in which they are set diametrically; expressed more simply, the pairs of rollers (like half-pulleys or sheaves) spin diametrically as does a coin when spun on the table. Then again, there are hollow-ended rivets which are clinched similar to a shoe eyelet. Others are a cross between a screw and a rivet. They have a very "quick" hardened thread, and you just drive them with a hammer—and they do not come out. Moreover, it must not be supposed that the demand for good reliable hand riveting is a thing of the past, and that all up-to-date work is done with electric or pneumatic tools. Far from it. There are plenty of places where such a tool could not be put to work, so the ability to perform with hand tools, creditably, is still an asset.

CHAPTER XIII

SOLDERING

HAVING now touched upon most of the operations in connection with ordinary sheet metal working, a few hints on the soldering of joints had, perhaps, best be given. Soldering is an act—I will not call it an *art*, as I may possibly be contradicted—in the joining of metals which many others have written about. Be that as it may; how many people *can* join a couple of pieces of metal together with anything approaching a properly soldered joint? Precious few, judging from such work as has come to my notice from time to time. Stick a knife under a corner and grip that raised corner with the pliers and one can rip the whole joint apart—"soldering"! In other cases so much solder has been stuck on and around, but rarely *between*, that upon re-soldering with the same solder, there has been sufficient surplus for two or three other jobs. Common confessions of failure are: "the thing won't stick" and "the iron won't pick the solder up."

Very often it is found that the two pieces that refused to "stick" had not been cleaned; often, that the iron that "will not pick up" has not been tinned, although the disconsolate solderer had watched a complete job being done, which certainly included tinning the iron.

There is a wide difference though between looking at a process and actually *seeing* it. One "sees" with one's mind, and if one's mind is not on the job, one misses half of what the eyes just "look at." Like most mechanical processes, unless you "get" the lot you may just as well "get" none.

Use either gas or an oil stove, or else the open fire. Special gas or charcoal tinmen's stoves are to be had, but some may possibly read these pages who are a long way from such amenities. Nearly everyone who has tools has a blowlamp.

It is an easy matter to rig up a stand for a couple of irons as shown in Fig. 32. Heating may also and equally well be done on a Primus or other oil stove. To conserve the heat, cut off a 6 in. piece of 5 in. or 6 in. channel iron. Lay it on the stove top plate and poke the iron or irons under that. When at long last it burns out, just cut another piece. Scrap, rusty stuff is as good as new—it will rust anyhow, new or old, with repeated heating and cooling.

Tinning the Bit

Heat the iron till it is painfully hot if held, say, 6 in. from the face—another plebeian method is to expectorate upon it and watch results. Should the moisture vanish with a hiss, then the iron is hot enough to "tin." Place the end on a firebrick and file the four facets of the point bright and clean. Dip quickly into either Baker's Fluid, Spirits of Salts, Fluxite, Tinol, Resin, Tallow, or any such fluxes, quickly apply the end of a stick of solder so that such molten solder flows over and covers the brightened end for about $\frac{3}{4}$ in. up the point, again dip in the flux and the bit is "tinned" and ready for use; it will "pick up" solder just as long as it is hot enough to melt it.

Do not keep a bit on the stove for hours on end; it will only burn the tinning away so that it will have to be done all over again. Besides this, it will deteriorate the copper bit or bolt (as we used to call it) and also make the handle uncomfortably hot.

The next procedure is to prepare a couple of pieces of metal for soldering so that they will "stick."

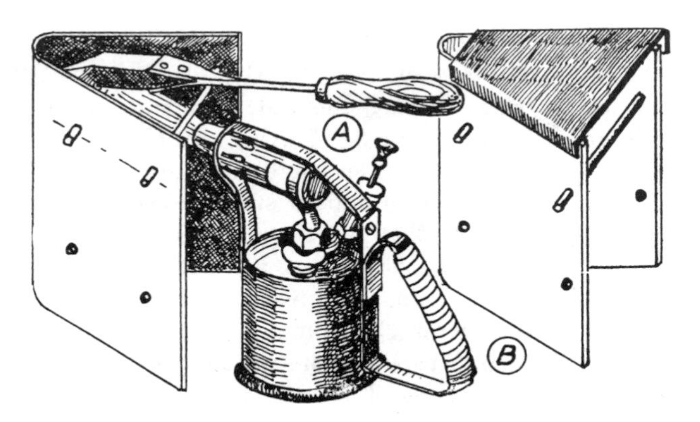

Piece of sheet iron bent to 60 deg. Rods just clearing blowlamp. Put set of holes in bottom to suit another size of lamp—reversed

With a lid on the device is very handy for warming a job—or sweating

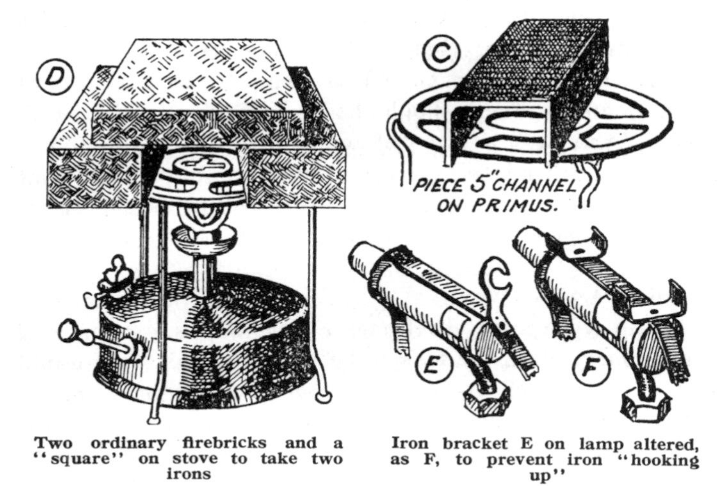

Two ordinary firebricks and a "square" on stove to take two irons

Iron bracket E on lamp altered, as F, to prevent iron "hooking up"

Fig. 32.—Makeshift soldering stoves

Tinning the Metal

Take each piece in turn, clean lightly with emery-cloth or a file, or by still another method, scraping, depending on the areas to be cleaned. Having done so, grip one corner or any part suitable, let the blowlamp or stove flame heat it gently for a few seconds if small, and for a minute or so if fairly bulky, then brush some fluid flux over it at a temperature which, though hot, will not instantaneously evaporate it. Next, run off a couple or so globules of solder from the solder-stick by means of the bit, hold the work over the flame to keep the heat, and persuade the solder to cover the cleaned portion just fluxed by means of the heated bit.

This it should do willingly enough, leaving a silvery coating all over. If you have to scrub and dig with your iron as if you were trying to rub a hole in the work—all to get the solder to "run"—something is wrong with the tinning or the iron. Maybe it is not hot enough, or not clean enough—it may even be greasy. The work must be clean—must be hot (but nothing like red-hot), and the iron must be properly tinned as well. Given this perfect state of affairs, there should be no difficulty in the world about "tinning" a piece of work.

A very good adage to keep in mind is: have your work as hot as your iron, and have one as clean as the other. "Clean" means "absolutely without dirt."

Tinning Large Work

To tin a piece of sheet metal (Fig. 33), say copper or brass, emery-cloth the face to be tinned, brush some liquid flux over it, catch up by one corner and lay three or four little "blobs" of solder at one end of the piece. Cant it up just clear of the actual flame and, applying the heated bit thereto, gently persuade and work the molten solder down towards the pliers—an old pair of course. When three parts of the way down, transfer the pliers to a portion already done and carry on until the whole sheet is covered. The residue will run along the bottom edge, when a quick wipe across with a tallowy rag whilst hot will leave the worker with a smoothly-tinned and silvery-looking sheet.

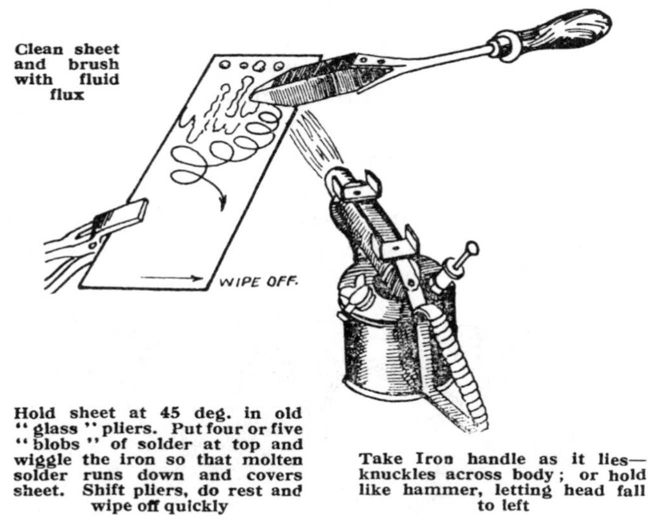

Fig. 33.—Tinning

Whether it is tinned with plain solder or with pure tin (for a domestic utensil) the processes are identical. Any flux will do as well, but I prefer a fluid flux for this type of work.

The secret of making uniform solder " blobs " is: not *too* hot an iron, hold the solder about $\frac{1}{2}$ in. off the plate, and keep the soldering iron and the solder together slowly moving along.

Years ago, as a youngster, I used to watch big domestic cooking utensils of copper, scratch-brushed clean and bright inside and fluxed with salamoniac crystals, tinned by melting block or stick tin in the heated pots and pans, quickly swilled round and as quickly wiped with a ball or wad of tallowy waste and the metal tipped from one to another—one man giving the final wipe round while his mate tinned and fluxed the next. There used to be quite a trade in those days doing dozens for big private houses and hotels.

Actually I prefer not to use a resinous flux for tinning large work that has to be heated, as such a flux is liable to "bake" on in a film and prevent the tinning "taking"; others may not experience this difficulty.

Fluxes for Different Metals

Galvanised iron goods—baths, buckets, tanks, and so on—are made up and then immersed in tanks or vats of molten zinc, such immersion generally doing the duty of "solder-

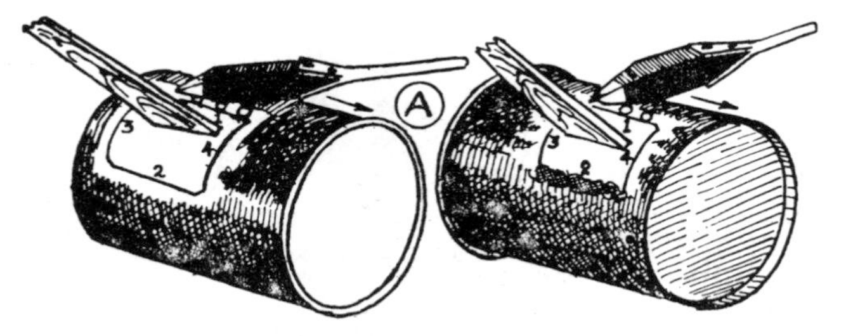

Having found trouble, scrape or clean off for a fair space around. Next, cut patch, trim corners. Tin job and patch, bending it a bit more than job. Press in place with wood, keeping edge of patch near top so that solder will flow under it. Turn over. Do opposite edge and then the ends

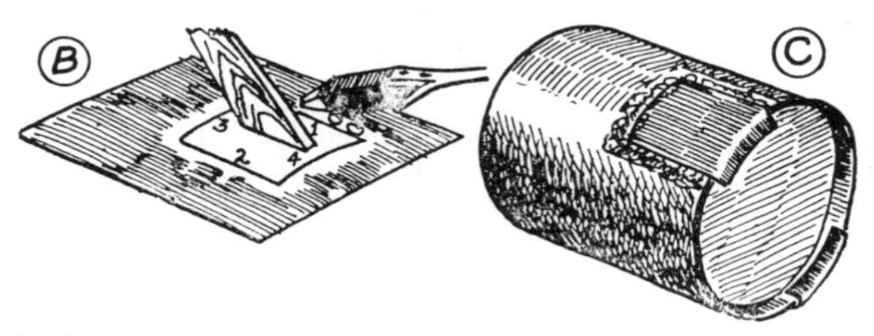

For flat patch use same method. Bend patch a little and hold down as shown. Then solder in order: 1, 2, 3, 4

In this case solder three sides, then hammer tongue over rim and solder there. Let iron "dwell" a while

Fig. 34.—Fixing a patch

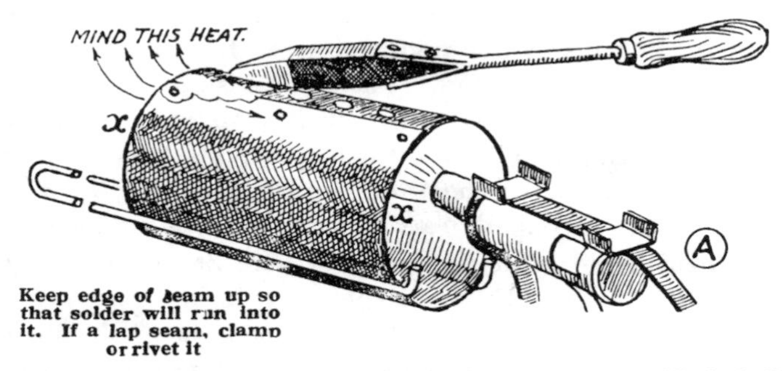

Keep edge of seam up so that solder will run into it. If a lap seam, clamp or rivet it

Grip at any point X—X with old "glass" pliers or support on "hairpin" as shown. Brush on flux, place "blobs" on seam. Let flame play gently on the under-side. Apply iron and lead molten solder down.

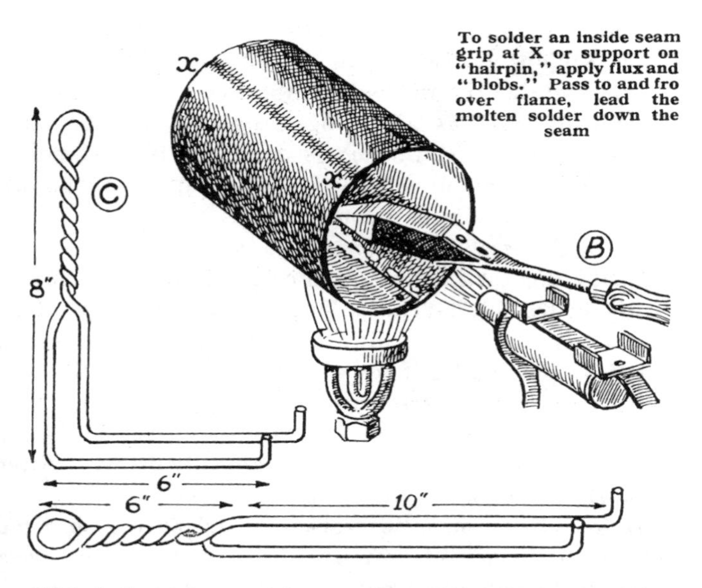

To solder an inside seam grip at X or support on "hairpin," apply flux and "blobs." Pass to and fro over flame, lead the molten solder down the seam

"Hairpin" of $\frac{1}{4}$ in. round iron

Use either "Primus" blow-lamp, or Bunsen burner

Fig. 35.—Soldering seams

ing" the seams pretty effectively. Those that are not thoroughly soldered are frequent cases for the tinsmith's or jobbing mechanic's shop. The trouble is often discovered before actual sale takes place, when the retailer has to effect the repair in his own tin-shop—if his business runs to such—or else have the work "done out."

Such repair, if properly carried out, *should* be near enough indistinguishable from the new article. Scrape the seam thoroughly clean with a sharply-ground half-round file; the tang half of a "six inch" is a handy size. Take care to get right into such a seam, even to the extent of drawing a sharp pointed tang along it both outside and inside. A light brushing of killed spirits (hydrochloric acid into which small pieces of zinc have been dissolved until the acid will no longer act and ebullition ceases) over the seam, a quick dipping of the heated bit into the acid pot, and with the bit lightly in contact with the solder stick, a neat trail of solder is laid along the seam. Do the same to the outer side and the job is done. It is good policy to clean the seams an inch each way clear of the known leaky part, to be sure of a sound repair.

Thoroughly wash afterwards, whether old or new.

Should a domestic utensil, such as a bath used for clothes washing, or bucket, have been long in use with soapy water, there is generally some difficulty in cleaning the seam. Proceed as previously, if for a seam, but use a little neat hydrochloric acid (as purchased from the chemist). This will immediately clean away any grease and act as a very potent flux, causing the solder to run very freely. After this, wash the work very thoroughly.

Certain articles, such as gear-cases and covers on some machines, are made of ordinary sheet steel. Motor cycle and car fuel tanks often require soldering: lugs come off, filler cap necks come adrift, and so on. With small components of a "non-petrol" type, if rusty at all, just file up or clean until bright, brush over with either Baker's or other similar flux, warm up with the flame and tin all over the part to be joined. Thoroughly scrape the other or major part and tin that also. If anything to do with petrol, that is if it is a container, do not have a light anywhere near it, and brush the soldering iron clean from sparks, hot soot, or anything that can cause ignition. See that the iron has no semblance of redness, and use spirits to tin the place where the piece is to be soldered, so that this may be done with the minimum of heat. One can use spirits effectively with much less heat than with other fluxes.

Speaking generally, there is no more difficulty in tinning steel or wrought iron sheet than any other metal. Care must be taken, however, to avoid oxidisation before oı during the tinning operation. Solder will not " take " properly when the metal is " blued " with heat, so you must tin quickly before that happens.

Steel in small portions is very easy to solder or tin. Sheet iron is not quite so meanable. Tinplate—thin steel-sheet, tinned—is just plain soldering, no need to scrape, just see that it is clean. Resin, Fluxite, Baker's or ordinary spirits will solder it equally well. Always wash it and dry it afterwards, otherwise it will rust. Where washing is precluded, use resin or Fluxite or tallow. Zinc is solderable with zinc-chloride or spirits of salts, the hydrochloric already mentioned. Zinc has a greasy nature, but there is no difficulty in soldering it. Rustless steel is equally easy to join, using spirits of salts, Baker's, or similar fluxes.

CHAPTER XIV

BRAZING

THE amount of sheet-metal brazing that the small shop dealing with ordinary repairs, will be asked to do is not likely to be very large. In fact, in the last ten or so years, I do not recall one occasion where the actual brazing of sheet metal was called for—not for " business," anyhow.

The main thing is the " spelter "—or the " solder " with which the joint is made. Small work may very conveniently be hard-soldered ; that is joined with the aid of considerable heat and a brazing medium known generally as silver-solder. There are at least seven grades of silver solder available. Number one, which contains the highest proportion of silver and is therefore the most expensive, melts at a dull red heat (620 deg. C.). It " flashes " very suddenly, forming neat but small fillets. Number two is very similar but contains slightly less silver; number three has a wider melting range, thus forming larger fillets, and so on up to number five, while the remaining two alloys have rather higher melting points and are more suitable for the brazing of copper or gunmetal.

Nearly all grades can now be obtained in a wide variety of strips or round wires, suitable for every type of job. The heat necessary can be provided by a blowlamp, an air-gas brazing torch or a bottled gas (Propane or Butane) blowpipe. Larger sheet-metal brazing is generally done with a very easy-running brass spelter—so easy running that it will melt and join thin sheet brass some time before the melting point of the latter is reached.

Needless to say, this spelter, like all others, must be used in conjunction with a flux which may be any of a number of proprietary brands, all of which, together with such spelters as may be required, can be obtained from engineers' sundries stores. The safest spelter for such work as sheet brass brazing is a grade of golden yellow which looks like filings. It is neither granular nor crystalline, as are some kinds of silver solder. This is used extensively in the scientific and nautical-instrument trade. In the latter connection it is used to braze up compass bowls, binnacle stands and tops, binnacle lamps and a host of other things peculiar to that trade, with ordinary borax and water as flux. The heating is best done over a portable forge burning coke. This gives very considerable heat from a clear fire, but such heat is over a wide area of metal and not concentrated in one particular place as is the heat of a blow-lamp or torch.

The work, according to its structure, is held over the fire with the spelter and borax (and I prefer this old-fashioned stuff) mixed with water distributed—" arranged " is a more exact description—along the seam following its zig-zag course. As the work heats up to a glowing redness, the spelter will melt and flow into the interstices. There may be a crackle or two as the borax bubbles and bursts, but an old hack saw blade will keep the bubbles from jumping too high, and lead them to where they can do the most good. The old hacksaw will also lay in place further supplies of water-soaked spelter or borax if needed for a sound joint.

The soaking of the spelter enables it to be picked up and laid without spilling. What with the heat, the weight (be it only a pound or so) of the work extended in tongs, and the certain degree of nervous strain incurred, your hand is likely to dither a little when ladling up a last dose of spelter. Should this be dry (or of the granulated variety) you will lose the run of half of it as it will dance about on (and off) the hacksaw blade like a pea on a hot shovel.

The mention of " nervous strain " may cause a certain degree of ribaldry, but by the time those guilty of such unseemly behaviour have held a brass cylinder, say 12 in.

long, at arm's length in a heavy tongs, facing a coke fire, reminiscent of Dante's Inferno at its best, reached for and picked up a saw blade-full of spelter and laid it unspilled in place, they will be thankful that it was moist enough to stay on the spatula or sawblade while they had it in transit.

Large cylindrical jobs should be bound round with two or three turns of iron wire at each end to prevent them springing apart under the influence of heat, such heat causing the dovetailed joints to open slightly. It should be said that the edges are filed thin before dovetailing. Similarly, other types of cylindrical work, narrow bands of fair diameter, and so on should be secured against expansive separation at the joint. This is most easily accomplished by squeezing together in the middle into a semblance of a figure eight, gripping the nipped-in portion in the tongs and brazing the seam, which is arranged, when bending, to come at the bottom centre of the figure eight. Nothing is more difficult to braze than, say, a narrow band or rim of about 20 or 22 gauge metal that dithers about all over the place, and the above method stiffens the job and prevents this (Fig. 36C.) As it is thoroughly annealed during the brazing operation, it is easily trued up again for the finishing operations.

Domes are brazed into cylindrical bodies, as, for example, the domed top of a ship's binnacle. The cylindrical part is first brazed up. Then the top part is closed in to about a 45 deg. angle, the edge dovetail-nicked all round and a dished or half-blocked disc of suitable diameter then inserted so as to lie on the lower tongues of the nicks ; the upper ones are closed down over the disc in a manner similar to Fig. 36, D and E. The work is then held over the fire in a pair of 90 deg. cranked-nosed tongs, and the fluxed and speltered joint brazed as sketch F. The operator has to watch the inside of the work all the time for his heat colours—bright red and no more. When it is understood that such a dome may be 15 in. and more in diameter, with a depth of 10 in., and that all this is held very awkwardly (of necessity) for

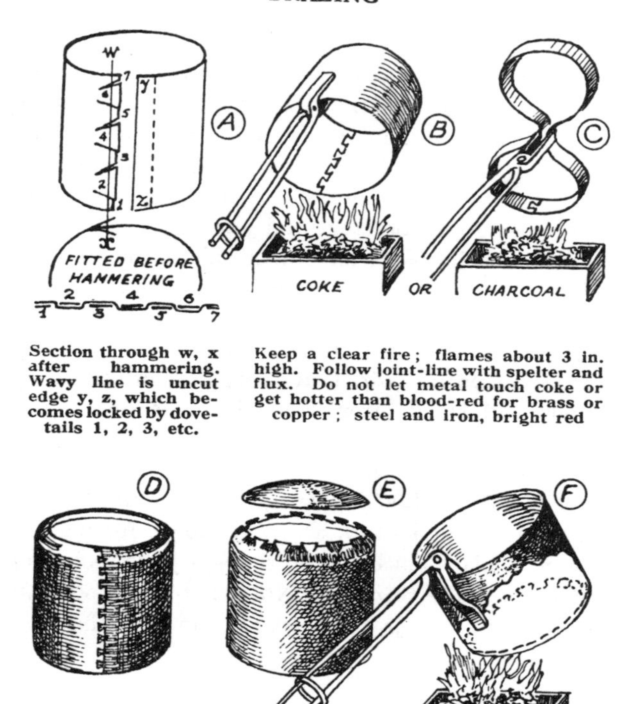

Section through w, x after hammering. Wavy line is uncut edge y, z, which becomes locked by dovetails 1, 2, 3, etc.

Keep a clear fire; flames about 3 in. high. Follow joint-line with spelter and flux. Do not let metal touch coke or get hotter than blood-red for brass or copper; steel and iron, bright red

After brazing cylinder and hammering seam enough to true up, place over dome stake and turn "in" the top as D. Mark off margin and cut dovetails, block a plate to fit as E. Knock down dovetails and braze up as F. Finally, hammer all seams on stakes to harden. File off any lumps

Fig. 36.—Brazing cylindrical jobs

some five or six minutes over a forge fire there is some excuse for a little "nervous strain" in those extremities before the job is finished.

After brazing, let the job lie in a tub or lead vat containing sulphuric acid—old battery acid is as good as anything if it can be obtained. This thoroughly cleans the work outside and in. Use a long stick with a bundle of rags tied thereto, and be careful of your eyes.

Having thoroughly cleaned the work, examine it for flaws in brazing. If a flaw is visible, locally braze again. If ever you are unfortunate enough to find a burnt hole, a patch must be brazed in position. If a hole appears during the first stage—through someone distracting your attention, possibly—just go on brazing, and patch after.

Everything being as it should be, place the work over a large dome head stake and file off any outstanding excrescences, and then hammer down the seam into conformation with the general curvature of the dome.

Finally, the work is wired, and any further constructional operations performed after which it takes up its position aboard ship and sails the ocean, if it happens to be a binnacle top or a compass bowl.

One or two pairs of 90 deg. tongs, made similarly to sketch F, in sizes 15 in. and 24 in. are very handy for many other jobs. A good blacksmith will do them or your tool merchant will get them made to order. Note that the top "handle" is "in one" with the jaw nearest ; *i.e.* outside the job.

CHAPTER XV

TANK CONSTRUCTION

IN Fig. 37 is shown a number of ways in which tanks or similar vessels may be made up. To save space, each tank is shown with odd ends, so that two methods may be dealt with in the same sketch.

Now, consider end A. This is the simplest of all ends and has been dealt with in earlier chapters on " edging " and " jenny-work." Such a tank, usually of the smaller type, is just soldered round the edge. Keep the tank canted slightly to help the flow of solder into the joint, use a liquid flux and lightly play the flame along the seam and on the " iron " meantime. With a good fitting cap, a neat little fillet of solder should show all round.

The end B is " set-in." Such an end is usually riveted as well as soldered, the latter procedure being effected from inside. Spill a teaspoonful of flux in the filler-cap hole, cant the job, let the flux run down to the end seam, roll it round a time or two and then drop half a dozen or so blobs of solder through after the flux. Apply the lamp at the lowest point (six-o'clock) and when solder begins to show at the edges of the shell and end, begin to roll the job slowly, playing the lamp on the work and keeping it inclined somewhere near the angle shown in Fig. 35B. If the rivets were well fitted and headed up very little solder will come through, but as I always desire " tightness " at first go I invariably sweat the rivets both sides at the one heat. Brush on some more Baker's, or whatever flux you use, space out a small pea-size blob of solder near (or on, if it will stay there) each head and just lay the soldering iron on it and watch. Done properly, that blob should collapse and flow evenly over the rivet head and leave a fillet all round it. In fact, the rivet will look like a pimple. Try to get them all looking like pimples—both sides—and that tank will cause you no misgivings after you have sent it out.

Another little tip before we close this job up, and it will also apply to others. Should the end be at all "easy" fitting just "bell" the end a little over the stake, or a mandrel and it will then "drive in" a nice fit with the mallet.

The dished end C is capped on also, and apart from the convexity, is like A. Procedure is the same. The dishing part has already been attended to in Chapter III, and needs no explanation. Of course, one will not dish a 15 in. end on a block hollowed, say, for a kettle lid. In fact, such ends may be very well done on a "flat" block as long as it is a fairly soft one. The repeated hammerings form a slight incidental concavity which is just right for this class of work.

In D is a dished end again, but notice the seam. The dish is edged backwards pressed into the tank, say a quarter inch inside the edge (previously tinned, of course), and lightly soldered from the outside. No lumps should appear; any surplus should be scraped off and the edge then knocked back over the edge of the "end." The final procedure is as B.

Example E is flat ended, but "turned in" as D. The end, however, is strengthened and backed up by a beaded groove. The idea was shown in Fig. 20 for a rectangular tank and a couple of similar applications of the roller gadget are featured in Figs. 31B and in Fig. 39. As explained therein, one man could not manoeuvre a big tank round on his own, so ways and means had to be evolved—even if they were comical. They may even be pre-historic, but they did the job finely. The other end, F, is similar but is dished as D. The soldering is done as for B or D, and if

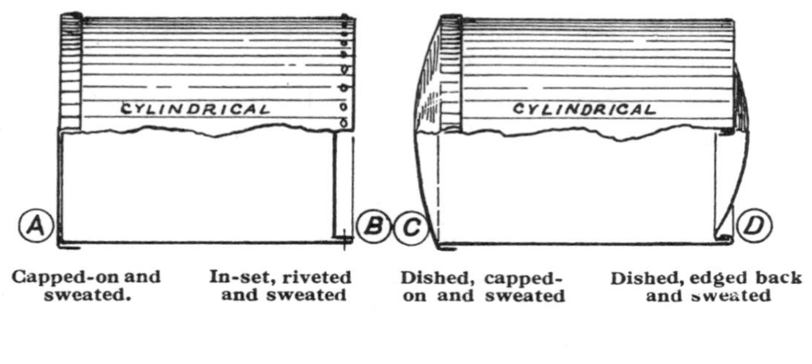

Capped-on and sweated. | In-set, riveted and sweated | Dished, capped-on and sweated | Dished, edged back and sweated

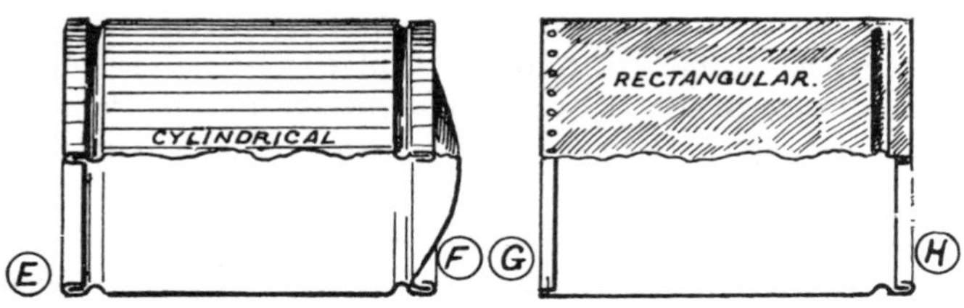

Edging similar to D, but ends backed up by beaded grooves

Rectangular tank. Ends similar to B and E

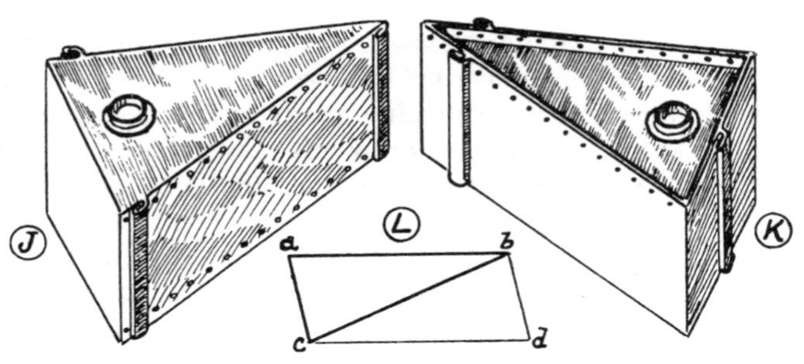

Top flush and set in first. Bottom is similar to top K. Three grooved side seams where tank dimensions make single-sheet construction impossible

Capacity of triangular topped tank abc. Think of it as rectangular. Area abcd is ac × ab; capacity of △ is half of ac × ab × depth in cub. in. or cub. ft.

Top and bottom inset. Three-seam construction for reasons J. In both cases rivet and thoroughly sweat. Cut holes and fit filler caps first

Fig. 37.—Tank construction

you wish to go all the way, you can run a fillet round the outer turned-in edge too.

G and H refer to rectangular tanks and are done in the same manner as B and E. The drilling for rivets is shown in Fig. 31A, and the beading rig-up is in Fig. 20. J and K are a couple of cases where tanks have to be made to fit special locations, say, either a water or fuel tank in a launch, " cruiser " or drifter. The tank stows away up for'ad, leaving other space, usually thus occupied, available for purposes more suitable—more engine space, perhaps, or more room in the cabin. A tank can be made to fit anywhere. In J and K the seams are differently placed, it will be noted. Why ? There is no very particular reason, except that such a size tank could not well be made from a single sided sheet . . . . unless specially rolled to order, which entails delay and somewhat more expense. Most big metal-people will roll you a special sheet, within limits, on receipt of specification. The trouble is, however, that most tank jobs are " rush " ones. And so the tank of this type, if not exactly many-coloured like Joseph's coat, is nevertheless made up like other coats—from more pieces than one. They all have to be wangled together to give the best results, and so the seamings differ. The whacking great seams shown, are, of course, not in proportion by a mile, and are shown just to indicate plainly the type. Where material permits, I never fancy a seam at a corner, nor in a position where such a seam cannot readily be got at should the unexpected happen. Again, it is easier to work seams in the positions K, and there is a clean bend at the fore end which looks a bit better. There is nothing difficult or impossible about the fore-end seam in J, though it may look queer. " How can anyone get a mandrel in there to work the seam ? " it may be asked. There is no need to do so. You just join two ends in that way, solder them and bend after, so that the back of the groove is in tension—actually pulling itself tighter. Being soldered, it will stay tight. The second seam on the far side is done in the same manner. It may be joined up when the first is done at the fore end, the fore end bent, then laid over a mandrel or in the bench bending bar shown in Fig. 2, and the second one done. The " hooks " of the third seam were done at the same time as the rest, accurately marked off, of course, in accordance with tank dimensions—and all that remains is just to hook this last together, lay it on the bench bar, fore end packed up so that it cannot swing (similarly to Fig. 30G) close the middle and then the ends with the grooved punch, mallet down, solder, and all is ready for the top and bottom to go in.

The inside dimensions are measured, and then transferred to a large sheet of the desired metal. It may be possible, after adding the edging allowance, to lay the patterns for top and bottom in such a manner as to cut both from the same sheet. A normal sheet is 4 ft. × 2 ft. remember; copper and brass sheets are readily obtained (other than " specials ") in larger sizes than that. Sketch L will illustrate this, though not intended for that purpose.

For ordinary purposes the finished tops and bottoms will come out all right if the nett pattern size is scribed out one sheet thickness " small " all round ; bent neatly on that line the turned-up edges make the size come right.

In any case it is better to err " small " than " big." You can always open out the edges, say, 1/16 in. out of square so that they will " fill the hole," whereas if the top or bottom came out 1/16 in. big all round you would buckle the sheet if you tried to force it within the sides. You can stretch the rim of a round job by hammer work, but to attempt this treatment on a straight sided job is asking for trouble. It is no joke to scrap (for the time being, anyhow) up to fifty shillings worth of metal and, say, a couple of days' wasted time, all because you began something you could not finish. Do not try stretching a straight sided tank unless you are an absolute metal magician.

The tank shown at J, it will be noted, has a " flush "

top and this obviously has to be fitted and riveted before the bottom is in place.

As a matter of fact, " top and bottom " means very little in such a case as this. Either way up makes but little difference—one surface must be a " hollow " one. Of course, this does not follow when the tank is large enough for a man to work inside as " holder-up "; but this comes under the heading of plater's or boilermaker's work, which is outside the province of this book.

The main disadvantage of a flush top or bottom from the point of view of the " small " worker, is that anyway he must do some holding-up. For very many of the rivets, the tank may be laid on its side, with the heads of the rivets inside and held on such a rig-up as shown in Fig. 30G—less the " crutch " but with a box under the lower corner to keep the side being worked upon level on the bench bar, such a shape being badly out of balance in any case. By using a chamfered bar it may be possible to work right up into the acute angle at the fore-end, but most likely the last two right in the apex will have to be fine thread bolts and nuts of rivet size ; the nuts inside and thoroughly sweated afterwards.

Again, if the metal be thick enough, these screws may be tapped direct into the inner flange. It may be thought that it is as well to tap through both thicknesses. It is not. Unless those two thicknesses can be brought right close together (and kept there) such " double-tapping " will only push the metals apart. So, where thickness permits, have the outer hole neat clearing size, tap the inner one, draw up tight and " sweat."

One real advantage of a flush top is that in a location where water is likely to drip on to such a tank there is no " hollow " in which it can accumulate and enter the filler cap.

Of course, this also may be prevented by using an extension on the filler fitting, but there are many cases in mind where such extensions were impossible, these tanks being jammed right up under a deck or floor and filled through a hole cut therein. " Wash-down " and " elemental " water leaking through the deck fitting soon makes a duck's pool on the tank top. One cannot screw down the tank cap tightly owing to cramped space on the top. If one did manage to " screw up " by a fluke, it would be exceedingly difficult to unscrew the thing. There is a limit to the strength of one's hand or even its ability to grip a spanner in a space, say, $2\frac{1}{2}$ in. high, and 18 in. inwards, at shoulder height. So it may be taken as fair advice in such cases, to have a flush topped tank.

Bottoms

If any tank has an exposed or damp position, the best kind of tank is the one with the flush top, and the actual bottom will then rest on the seam edges—sketch 37K inverted.

For ease of handling in confined spaces the flush bottom is the winner. It can be pushed any way about over timbers and framed up supports with no edges to " hang up " against nails, knots, jutting tenons or joint edges. If some-one accidentally " let's go " before time, less damage is done to trapped fingers.

It will by now be clear that in the choice of a tank, or in the making of one, the various pros and cons must be weighed very carefully ; the final decision depending upon what will be the best in the long run.

It is, of course, generally understood that all holes for fittings are cut *before* the tank is assembled. Flanged filler fittings are riveted thereto before the tanks are closed right up so that a hold-up can be easily used for such rivets as may be necessary. Even on very large tanks, larger than any " sheet " metal worker will have to make anyway, the thickness rarely exceeds that known as " eighth plate."

To screw heavy manhole rings or filler flanges to this from outside gives little chance to the threads which are at least 5/16 in. Whit. or B.S.F. Other ways and means are discussed later. In thinner and smaller tanks, to cut any hole of reasonable size after the tank is made, is quite a job of work, and rarely will a fitting lie flat thereon afterwards.

Soldering in place leaves the tank top (if it is a flat one) like hills and valleys, buckled with heat. Plain " iron " soldering, with no blow lamp, is merely *tacking* such a fitting—it is not really soldered, and may even come off as the tank " settles down."

Fig. 38 illustrates some " wangles " whereby internal fittings were placed inside the tank after construction.

There is no " patent " about it, but I have certainly never seen anyone do it before, nor, for that matter, ever heard of the trick being done. It is a trick—nothing more or less.

The reason it had to be done was that certain locations precluded the rigging of supports, nor were straps and long bolts practicable. It meant either slinging it from inside its top, or having another one made. To sling without reinforcing was simply asking for trouble, and, as shown, even with the plates taking the " pull " I should think twice before passing more than a fifteen gallon one slung that way.

Actually, a 10 gall. size in the present case stood up well—no appreciable sag being noticeable. Taking $6\frac{1}{4}$ gall. to the cubic foot, a tank 24 in. $\times$ 12 in. $\times$ 12 in. is $12\frac{1}{2}$ gall. capacity, and 18 or 20 g. brass makes a terribly stiff job in a tank this size.

The final fixing holes through the tank top into the bars or plates may be drilled from actual measurements, or else a piece of thick brown paper (tank size) may be placed under the surface intended to hold the tank and the existing or purposely drilled holes rubbed into the paper, cut out and used on the tank top as a template.

Such a paper template may be taken from the tank itself if all holes are present therein, and this template used

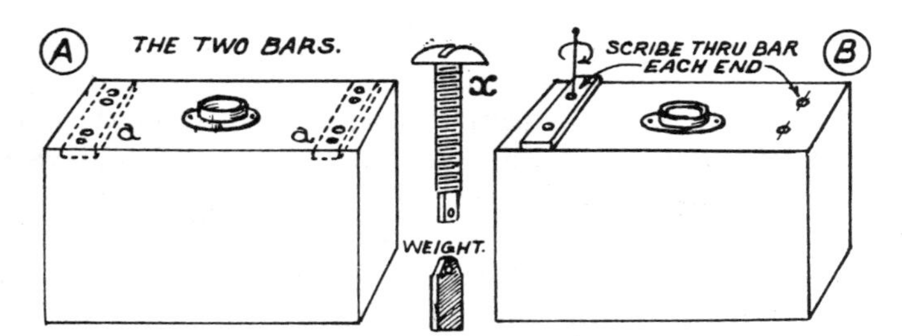

The two bars a, a have to be fixed inside the tank, screwed in place so that other holes may be drilled and tapped for bolts to hold up tank in use

Being alike, use one as template. Scribe through the holes on to tank each end and drill "clearing" size for such screws as are desired to fix these bars in place

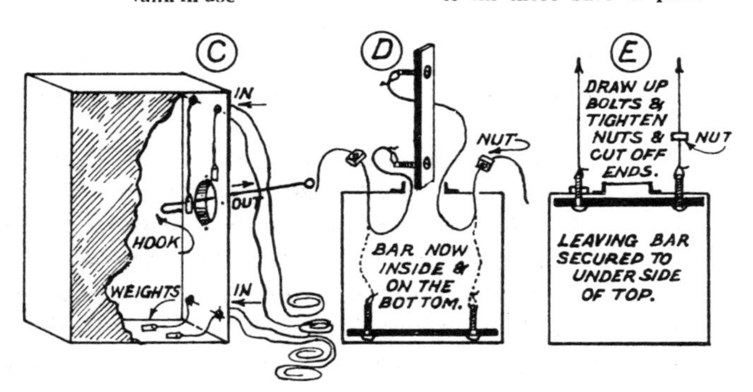

File flats on four screws x and drill ends. Four small weights to go through screw holes on thread. Poke through holes and "wangle" tank so that they swing past filler hole. Hook through reverse tank and hook out other pair, as C. Fit screws to bar. Cut off weights and tie on screws. Drop bar through filler as D

Let go gently down to avoid breaking threads. Run on the nuts and see loose ends do not go back down screw holes. Now E. Get someone to pull up both threads at once, "wangle" screws through holes and hold there. Let nuts run down threads on to screws. Nut up and cut off

Fig. 38.—Securing fittings in tanks

to locate the supporting holes in the ceiling, underside of deck or platform from which it is desired to hang the job.

Fixing Filler Reinforcing Ring Inside

Another trick of similar nature, which may have a wider and more useful application, is the fixing of a reinforcing ring inside a tank to secure a heavy filler flange by screwing. Such a ring is generally about 6 in. in diameter—anyway, the same size as the filler flange, which is usually a galvanised commercial pipe-flange, this often being fitted with a special cap or plug.

The hole in the tank top is, we may take it, round about 2 in. diameter, may be $2\frac{1}{2}$ in., rarely more. You have to put a 6 in. ring inside the tank through that.

Clamp the " ring " to the filler flange (or scribe through and mark the holes) and drill so that the holes in both agree ; mark so that you can pick up the mating holes later on. Tap to suit screws. Lay the flange on the tank and drill the holes through that and mark again, so that you can pick up the right fixing later on. Now grip the reinforcing ring in the vice and cut it in two across the middle between two holes, keeping that locating mark still in mind.

Next stick a couple of lengths of string or fishing line *down* through a pair of holes in the tank agreeing with similar holes in that half of the ring. Fish the ends *up* through the filler hole. Thread string through the mating holes in the half ring, taking care that this half faces the way it is going to lie when fixed inside. Tie a small washer on each string so that the half-ring cannot drop off, or the string pull through before you are ready. (You can even tie a couple of knots, as long as they are big enough to jam behind the screw holes.)

The next part of the business is very similar to Fig. 38. Your washers or knots take the place of screws X, and you just need to poke the string down about three inches or so before catching with long-nosed pliers or hooked wire, so weights are not needed in this case.

Drop the " half ring " back, down the filler hole, keep hold of the string ends, thread on the main flange now, (making sure that it is the right way about) and draw up the strings until you hear the half-ring sound against the underside. Make sure that the strings are not twisted and that everything is "nice" inside. That being so, insert a screw down through the flange, wiggle it into the corresponding hole in the half ring and screw up just easy for

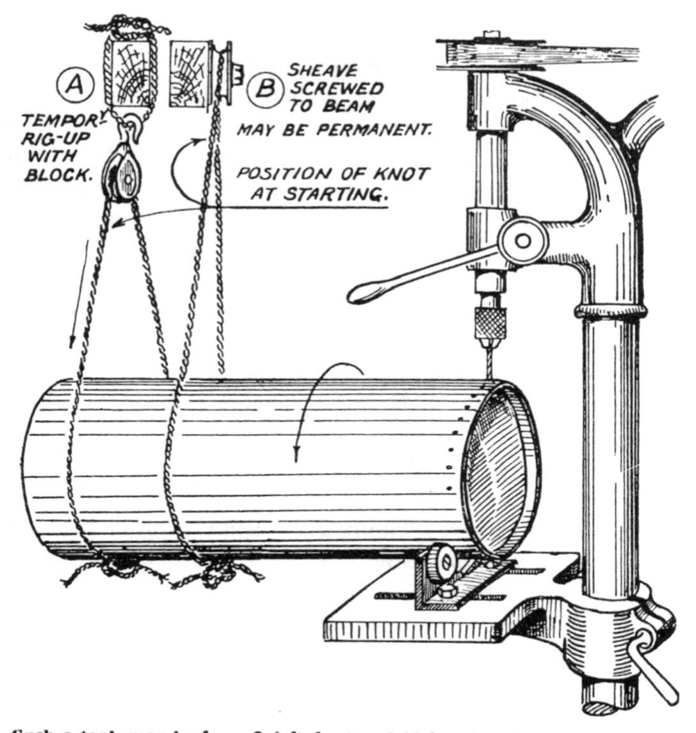

Such a tank may be from 3-6 ft. long and 18 in. diam. Sling up level as shown—either way, though B can be permanent—rotate towards operator and drill on rollers

Fig. 39.—Drilling a cylinder or tank

the present. Note that this screw goes into a hole somewhere midway between the strings—it depends upon the number of holes. You may be able to use a couple of "first-fixing" screws.

The flange is now where it should be and the half-ring is

screwed tentatively to it. Remove the strings. Repeat the string operation on the other half ring ; this time, poking it down through the flange itself. Draw up tight as before, though now you must wangle this one so that its horns do not foul those of the one that is fixed. You can juggle it so it comes " right " with a scriber, file tang, small marlinspike or the like, down through one of the screw holes.

As soon as everything is satisfactory underneath, insert a screw or two as before and set up just easy. Fish out the strings backwards. Wangle all screwholes so they show " fair," run a tap through part way (and above all, do *not* drop it inside) to make sure, and finally insert and tighten up all screws.

A fine seal for such jobs as this is red lead powder mixed with shellac varnish to a stiff creamy consistency. Make a little heap of red lead, scoop a hollow in it with a knife blade or something similar, and pour on shellac. A little at first, mixing and adding shellac until the consistency is right. Smear all jointing surfaces and threads, tighten down, wipe off neatly and clean. It dries quickly and hard, and it makes a fine joint. Thoroughly clean your fingers and nail crevices, and be careful of cuts, for this mixture is rank poison. Methylated is fine for cleaning it off fingers.